**Teacher Edition**

# Eureka Math®
# Grade 5
# Module 1

Special thanks go to the Gordon A. Cain Center and to the Department of Mathematics at Louisiana State University for their support in the development of *Eureka Math*.

For a free *Eureka Math* Teacher
Resource Pack, Parent Tip
Sheets, and more please visit
https://eurekamath.greatminds.org/teacher-resource-pack

**Eureka Math: *A Story of Units*® Contributors**

Katrina Abdussalaam, Curriculum Writer
Tiah Alphonso, Program Manager—Curriculum Production
Kelly Alsup, Lead Writer / Editor, Grade 4
Catriona Anderson, Program Manager—Implementation Support
Debbie Andorka-Aceves, Curriculum Writer
Eric Angel, Curriculum Writer
Leslie Arceneaux, Lead Writer / Editor, Grade 5
Kate McGill Austin, Lead Writer / Editor, Grades PreK–K
Adam Baker, Lead Writer / Editor, Grade 5
Scott Baldridge, Lead Mathematician and Lead Curriculum Writer
Beth Barnes, Curriculum Writer
Bonnie Bergstresser, Math Auditor
Bill Davidson, Fluency Specialist
Jill Diniz, Program Director
Nancy Diorio, Curriculum Writer
Nancy Doorey, Assessment Advisor
Lacy Endo-Peery, Lead Writer / Editor, Grades PreK–K
Ana Estela, Curriculum Writer
Lessa Faltermann, Math Auditor
Janice Fan, Curriculum Writer
Ellen Fort, Math Auditor
Peggy Golden, Curriculum Writer
Maria Gomes, Pre-Kindergarten Practitioner
Pam Goodner, Curriculum Writer
Greg Gorman, Curriculum Writer
Melanie Gutierrez, Curriculum Writer
Bob Hollister, Math Auditor
Kelley Isinger, Curriculum Writer
Nuhad Jamal, Curriculum Writer
Mary Jones, Lead Writer / Editor, Grade 4
Halle Kananak, Curriculum Writer
Susan Lee, Lead Writer / Editor, Grade 3
Jennifer Loftin, Program Manager—Professional Development
Soo Jin Lu, Curriculum Writer
Nell McAnelly, Project Director

# Mathematics Curriculum

## Table of Contents

# GRADE 5 • MODULE 1

## Place Value and Decimal Fractions

# Grade 5 • Module 1

# Place Value and Decimal Fractions

## OVERVIEW

In Module 1, students' understandings of the patterns in the base ten system are extended from Grade 4's work with place value to include decimals to the thousandths place. In Grade 5, students deepen their knowledge through a more generalized understanding of the relationships between and among adjacent places on the place value chart, e.g., 1 tenth times any digit on the place value chart moves the digit one place value to the right (**5.NBT.1**). Toward the module's end, students apply these new understandings as they reason about and perform decimal operations through the hundredths place.

Topic A opens the module with a conceptual exploration of the multiplicative patterns of the base ten system using place value disks and a place value chart. Students notice that multiplying by 1,000 is the same as multiplying by $10 \times 10 \times 10$. Since each factor of 10 shifts the digits one place to the left, multiplying by $10 \times 10 \times 10$—which can be recorded in exponential form as $10^3$ (**5.NBT.2**)—shifts the position of the digits to the left 3 places, thus changing the digits' relationships to the decimal point (**5.NBT.2**). Application of these place value understandings to problem solving with metric conversions completes Topic A (**5.MD.1**).

Topic B moves into the naming of decimal fraction numbers in expanded, unit (e.g., 4.23 = 4 ones 2 tenths 3 hundredths), and word forms and concludes with using like units to compare decimal fractions. Now, in Grade 5, students use exponents and the unit fraction to represent expanded form (e.g., $2 \times 10^2 + 3 \times (\frac{1}{10}) + 4 \times (\frac{1}{100})$ = 200.34) (**5.NBT.3**). Further, students reason about differences in the values of like place value units and express those comparisons with symbols (>, <, and =). Students generalize their knowledge of rounding whole numbers to round decimal numbers in Topic C, initially using a vertical number line to interpret the result as an approximation and then eventually moving away from the visual model (**5.NBT.4**).

In the latter topics of Module 1, students use the relationships of adjacent units and generalize whole-number algorithms to decimal fraction operations (**5.NBT.7**). Topic D uses unit form to connect general methods for addition and subtraction with whole numbers to decimal addition and subtraction (e.g., 7 tens + 8 tens = 15 tens = 150 is analogous to 7 tenths + 8 tenths = 15 tenths = 1.5).

Topic E bridges the gap between Grade 4 work with multiplication and the standard algorithm by focusing on an intermediate step—reasoning about multiplying a decimal by a one-digit whole number. The area model, with which students have had extensive experience since Grade 3, is used as a scaffold for this work.

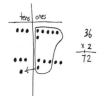
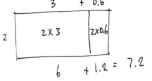
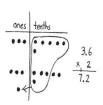

Topic F concludes Module 1 with a similar exploration of division of decimal numbers by one-digit whole-number divisors. Students solidify their skills with an understanding of the algorithm before moving on to long division involving two-digit divisors in Module 2.

The Mid-Module Assessment follows Topic C. The End-of-Module Assessment follows Topic F.

## Notes on Pacing for Differentiation

If pacing is a challenge, consider the following modifications and omissions. Consolidate Lessons 9 and 10 because these lessons devote a day each to adding and subtracting with decimals. If students are fluent with addition and subtraction with whole numbers and their understanding of decimal place value is strong (from Grade 4 Module 6 and Grade 5 Module 1 Topic B), practicing both addition and subtraction with decimals can be done in one lesson. Begin assessing students' skill with addition and subtraction with whole numbers during the fluency activity of Lesson 5, and spend a series of days doing so.

**Distribution of Instructional Minutes**

This diagram represents a suggested distribution of instructional minutes based on the emphasis of particular lesson components in different lessons throughout the module.

■ Fluency Practice
■ Concept Development
■ Application Problems
■ Student Debrief

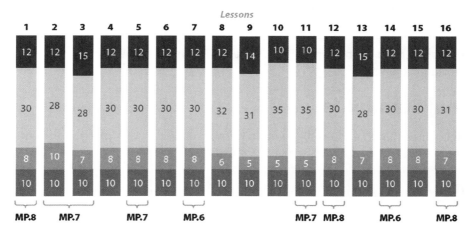

MP = Mathematical Practice

## Focus Grade Level Standards

### Understand the place value system.

**5.NBT.1**    Recognize that in a multi-digit number, a digit in one place represents 10 times as much as it represents in the place to its right and 1/10 of what it represents in the place to its left.

**5.NBT.2**    Explain patterns in the number of zeros of the product when multiplying a number by powers of 10, and explain patterns in the placement of the decimal point when a decimal is multiplied or divided by a power of 10. Use whole-number exponents to denote powers of 10.

**5.NBT.3**    Read, write, and compare decimals to thousandths.

    a.  Read and write decimals to thousandths using base-ten numerals, number names, and expanded form, e.g., $347.392 = 3 \times 100 + 4 \times 10 + 7 \times 1 + 3 \times (1/10) + 9 \times (1/100) + 2 \times (1/1000)$.

    b.  Compare two decimals to thousandths based on meanings of the digits in each place, using >, =, and < symbols to record the results of comparisons.

**5.NBT.4**    Use place value understanding to round decimals to any place.

## Perform operations with multi-digit whole numbers and with decimals to hundredths.[1]

**5.NBT.7**    Add, subtract, multiply, and divide decimals to hundredths, using concrete models or drawings and strategies based on place value, properties of operations, and/or the relationship between addition and subtraction; relate the strategy to a written method and explain the reasoning used.

## Convert like measurement units within a given measurement system.

**5.MD.1**    Convert among different-sized standard measurement units within a given measurement system (e.g., convert 5 cm to 0.05 m), and use these conversions in solving multi-step, real world problems.[2]

# Foundational Standards

**4.NBT.1**    Recognize that in a multi-digit whole number, a digit in one place represents ten times what it represents in the place to its right. *For example, recognize that 700 ÷ 70 = 10 by applying concepts of place value and division.*

**4.NBT.3**    Use place value understanding to round multi-digit whole numbers to any place.

**4.NF.5**    Express a fraction with denominator 10 as an equivalent fraction with denominator 100, and use this technique to add two fractions with respective denominators 10 and 100. (Students who can generate equivalent fractions can develop strategies for adding fractions with unlike denominators in general. But addition and subtraction with unlike denominators in general is not a requirement at this grade.) *For example, express 3/10 as 30/100, and add 3/10 + 4/100 = 34/100.*

**4.NF.6**    Use decimal notation for fractions with denominators 10 or 100. *For example, rewrite 0.62 as 62/100; describe a length as 0.62 meters; locate 0.62 on a number line diagram.*

**4.NF.7**    Compare two decimals to hundredths by reasoning about their size. Recognize that comparisons are valid only when the two decimals refer to the same whole. Record the results of comparisons with the symbols >, =, or <, and justify the conclusions, e.g., by using a visual model.

---

[1]The balance of this cluster is addressed in Module 2.

[2]The focus in this module is on the metric system to reinforce place value and writing measurements using mixed units. This standard is addressed again in later modules.

---

**4.MD.1**     Know relative sizes of measurement units within one system of units including km, m, cm; kg, g; lb, oz.; l, ml; hr, min, sec. Within a single system of measurement, express measurements in a larger unit in terms of a smaller unit. Record measurement equivalents in a two-column table. *For example, know that 1 ft is 12 times as long as 1 in. Express the length of a 4 ft snake as 48 in. Generate a conversion table for feet and inches listing the number pairs (1, 12), (2, 24), (3, 36), …*

**4.MD.2**     Use the four operations to solve word problems involving distances, intervals of time, liquid volumes, masses of objects, and money, including problems involving simple fractions or decimals, and problems that require expressing measurements given in a larger unit in terms of a smaller unit. Represent measurement quantities using diagrams such as number line diagrams that feature a measurement scale.

## Focus Standards for Mathematical Practice

**MP.6**     **Attend to precision.** Students express the units of the base ten system as they work with decimal operations, expressing decompositions and compositions with understanding (e.g., "9 hundredths + 4 hundredths = 13 hundredths. I can change 10 hundredths to make 1 tenth").

**MP.7**     **Look for and make use of structure.** Students explore the multiplicative patterns of the base ten system when they use place value charts and disks to highlight the relationships between adjacent places. Students also use patterns to name decimal fraction numbers in expanded, unit, and word forms.

**MP.8**     **Look for and express regularity in repeated reasoning.** Students express regularity in repeated reasoning when they look for and use whole-number general methods to add and subtract decimals and when they multiply and divide decimals by whole numbers. Students also use powers of ten to explain patterns in the placement of the decimal point and generalize their knowledge of rounding whole numbers to round decimal numbers.

## Overview of Module Topics and Lesson Objectives

| Standards | Topics and Objectives | | Days |
|---|---|---|---|
| **5.NBT.1**<br>**5.NBT.2**<br>**5.MD.1** | A | **Multiplicative Patterns on the Place Value Chart** | 4 |
| | | Lesson 1:   Reason concretely and pictorially using place value understanding to relate adjacent base ten units from millions to thousandths. | |
| | | Lesson 2:   Reason abstractly using place value understanding to relate adjacent base ten units from millions to thousandths. | |
| | | Lesson 3:   Use exponents to name place value units and explain patterns in the placement of the decimal point. | |
| | | Lesson 4:   Use exponents to denote powers of 10 with application to metric conversions. | |

| Standards | | Topics and Objectives | Days |
|---|---|---|---|
| **5.NBT.3** | B | **Decimal Fractions and Place Value Patterns**<br><br>Lesson 5:    Name decimal fractions in expanded, unit, and word forms by applying place value reasoning.<br><br>Lesson 6:    Compare decimal fractions to the thousandths using like units, and express comparisons with >, <, =. | 2 |
| **5.NBT.4** | C | **Place Value and Rounding Decimal Fractions**<br><br>Lessons 7–8:    Round a given decimal to any place using place value understanding and the vertical number line. | 2 |
| | | Mid-Module Assessment: Topics A–C (assessment ½ day, return ½ day, remediation or further applications 1 day) | 2 |
| **5.NBT.2**<br>**5.NBT.3**<br>**5.NBT.7** | D | **Adding and Subtracting Decimals**<br><br>Lesson 9:    Add decimals using place value strategies and relate those strategies to a written method.<br><br>Lesson 10:    Subtract decimals using place value strategies and relate those strategies to a written method. | 2 |
| **5.NBT.2**<br>**5.NBT.3**<br>**5.NBT.7** | E | **Multiplying Decimals**<br><br>Lesson 11:    Multiply a decimal fraction by single-digit whole numbers, relate to a written method through application of the area model and place value understanding, and explain the reasoning used.<br><br>Lesson 12:    Multiply a decimal fraction by single-digit whole numbers, including using estimation to confirm the placement of the decimal point. | 2 |
| **5.NBT.3**<br>**5.NBT.7** | F | **Dividing Decimals**<br><br>Lesson 13:    Divide decimals by single-digit whole numbers involving easily identifiable multiples using place value understanding and relate to a written method.<br><br>Lesson 14:    Divide decimals with a remainder using place value understanding and relate to a written method.<br><br>Lesson 15:    Divide decimals using place value understanding including remainders in the smallest unit.<br><br>Lesson 16:    Solve word problems using decimal operations. | 4 |
| | | End-of-Module Assessment: Topics A–F (assessment ½ day, return ½ day, remediation or further applications 1 day) | 2 |
| **Total Number of Instructional Days** | | | **20** |

# Terminology

## New or Recently Introduced Terms

- Exponent (how many times a number is to be used in a multiplication sentence)
- Millimeter (a metric unit of length equal to one-thousandth of a meter)
- Thousandths (related to place value)

## Familiar Terms and Symbols[3]

- >, <, = (greater than, less than, equal to)
- Base ten units (place value units)
- Bundling, making, renaming, changing, regrouping, trading
- Centimeter (cm, a unit of measure equal to one-hundredth of a meter)
- Digit (any of the numbers 0 to 9; e.g., what is the value of the digit in the tens place?)
- Expanded form (e.g., $135 = 1 \times 100 + 3 \times 10 + 5 \times 1$)
- Hundredths (as related to place value)
- Number line (a line marked with numbers at evenly spaced intervals)
- Number sentence (e.g., $4 + 3 = 7$)
- Place value (the numerical value that a digit has by virtue of its position in a number)
- Standard form (a number written in the format: 135)
- Tenths (as related to place value)
- Unbundling, breaking, renaming, changing, regrouping, trading
- Unit form (e.g., 3.21 = 3 ones 2 tenths 1 hundredth)
- Word form (e.g., one hundred thirty-five)

**NOTES ON**
*EXPRESSION, EQUATION,*
*AND NUMBER SENTENCE:*

Please note the descriptions for the following terms, which are frequently misused.

- **Expression:** A number, or any combination of sums, differences, products, or divisions of numbers that evaluates to a number (e.g., $3 + 4$, $8 \times 3$, $15 \div 3$ as distinct from an equation or number sentence).

- **Equation:** A statement that two expressions are equal (e.g., $3 \times \underline{\quad} = 12$, $5 \times b = 20$, $3 + 2 = 5$).

- **Number sentence** (also addition, subtraction, multiplication, or division sentence): An equation or inequality for which both expressions are numerical and can be evaluated to a single number (e.g., $4 + 3 = 6 + 1$, $2 = 2$, $21 > 7 \times 2$, $5 \div 5 = 1$). Number sentences are either true or false (e.g., $4 + 4 < 6 \times 2$ and $21 \div 7 = 4$) and contain no unknowns.

# Suggested Tools and Representations

- Number lines (a variety of templates, including a large one for the back wall of the classroom)
- Place value charts (at least one per student for an insert in their personal board)
- Place value disks

---

[3]These are terms and symbols students have used or seen previously.

# Suggested Methods of Instructional Delivery

## Directions for Administration of Sprints

Sprints are designed to develop fluency. They should be fun, adrenaline-rich activities that intentionally build energy and excitement. A fast pace is essential. During Sprint administration, teachers assume the role of athletic coaches. A rousing routine fuels students' motivation to do their personal best. Student recognition of increasing success is critical, and so every improvement is celebrated.

One Sprint has two parts with closely related problems on each. Students complete the two parts of the Sprint in quick succession with the goal of improving on the second part, even if only by one more.

With practice, the following routine takes about 9 minutes.

### Sprint A

Pass Sprint A out quickly, face down on student desks with instructions to not look at the problems until the signal is given. (Some Sprints include words. If necessary, prior to starting the Sprint, quickly review the words so that reading difficulty does not slow students down.)

- T:  You will have 60 seconds to do as many problems as you can. I do not expect you to finish all of them. Just do as many as you can, your personal best. (If some students are likely to finish before time is up, assign a number to count by on the back.)
- T:  Take your mark! Get set! THINK!

Students immediately turn papers over and work furiously to finish as many problems as they can in 60 seconds. Time precisely.

- T:  Stop! Circle the last problem you did. I will read just the answers. If you got it right, call out "Yes!" If you made a mistake, circle it. Ready?
- T:  (Energetically, rapid-fire call the first answer.)
- S:  Yes!
- T:  (Energetically, rapid-fire call the second answer.)
- S:  Yes!

Repeat to the end of Sprint A or until no student has a correct answer. If needed, read the count-by answers in the same way the Sprint answers were read. Each number counted-by on the back is considered a correct answer.

- T:  Fantastic! Now, write the number you got correct at the top of your page. This is your personal goal for Sprint B.
- T:  How many of you got one right? (All hands should go up.)
- T:  Keep your hand up until I say the number that is one more than the number you got correct. So, if you got 14 correct, when I say 15, your hand goes down. Ready?
- T:  (Continue quickly.) How many got two correct? Three? Four? Five? (Continue until all hands are down.)

If the class needs more practice with Sprint A, continue with the optional routine presented below.

- T:  I'll give you one minute to do more problems on this half of the Sprint. If you finish, stand behind your chair.

---

© 2015 Great Minds. eureka-math.org
G5-M1-TE-B1-1.3.1-1.2016

As students work, the student who scored highest on Sprint A might pass out Sprint B.

T:   Stop! I will read just the answers. If you got it right, call out "Yes!" If you made a mistake, circle it. Ready? (Read the answers to the first half again as students stand.)

**Movement**

To keep the energy and fun going, always do a stretch or a movement game in between Sprints A and B. For example, the class might do jumping jacks while skip-counting by 5 for about 1 minute. Feeling invigorated, students take their seats for Sprint B, ready to make every effort to complete more problems this time.

**Sprint B**

Pass Sprint B out quickly, face down on student desks with instructions not to look at the problems until the signal is given. (Repeat the procedure for Sprint A up through the show of hands for how many are right.)

T:   Stand up if you got more correct on the second Sprint than on the first.
S:   (Stand.)
T:   Keep standing until I say the number that tells how many more you got right on Sprint B. If you got three more right on Sprint B than you did on Sprint A, when I say *three,* you sit down. Ready? (Call out numbers starting with one. Students sit as the number by which they improved is called. Celebrate the students who improved most with a cheer.)
T:   Well done! Now, take a moment to go back and correct your mistakes. Think about what patterns you noticed in today's Sprint.
T:   How did the patterns help you get better at solving the problems?
T:   Rally Robin your thinking with your partner for 1 minute. Go!

Rally Robin is a style of sharing in which partners trade information back and forth, one statement at a time per person, for about 1 minute. This is an especially valuable part of the routine for students who benefit from their friends' support to identify patterns and try new strategies.

Students may take Sprints home.

## RDW or Read, Draw, Write (an Equation and a Statement)

Mathematicians and teachers suggest a simple process applicable to all grades:

1.   Read.
2.   Draw and label.
3.   Write an equation.
4.   Write a word sentence (statement).

The more students participate in reasoning through problems with a systematic approach, the more they internalize those behaviors and thought processes.

- What do I see?
- Can I draw something?
- What conclusions can I make from my drawing?

| Modeling with Interactive Questioning | Guided Practice | Independent Practice |
|---|---|---|
| The teacher models the whole process with interactive questioning, some choral response, and talk moves such as, "What did Monique say, everyone?" After completing the problem, students might reflect with a partner on the steps they used to solve the problem. "Students, think back on what we did to solve this problem. What did we do first?" Students might then be given the same or similar problem to solve for homework. | Each student has a copy of the question. Though guided by the teacher, they work independently at times and then come together again. Timing is important. Students might hear, "You have 2 minutes to do your drawing." Or, "Put your pencils down. Time to work together again." The Debrief might include selecting different student work to share. | Students are given a problem to solve and possibly a designated amount of time to solve it. The teacher circulates, supports, and thinks about which student work to show to support the mathematical objectives of the lesson. When sharing student work, students are encouraged to think about the work with questions such as, "What do you notice about Jeremy's work?", "What is the same about Jeremy's work and Sara's work?", "How did Jeremy show the $\frac{3}{7}$ of the students?", and "How did Sara show the $\frac{3}{7}$ of the students?" |

## Personal White Boards

### Materials Needed for Personal White Boards

    1 heavy duty clear sheet protector
    1 piece of stiff red tag board 11" × 8 ¼"
    1 piece of stiff white tag board 11" × 8 ¼"
    1 3" × 3" piece of dark synthetic cloth for an eraser (e.g., felt)
    1 low odor blue dry erase marker, fine point

### Directions for Creating Personal White Boards

Cut the white and red tag to specifications. Slide into the sheet protector. Store the eraser on the red side. Store markers in a separate container to avoid stretching the sheet protector.

### Frequently Asked Questions About Personal White Boards

*Why is one side red and one white?*

- The white side of the board is the "paper." Students generally write on it, and if working individually, turn the board over to signal to the teacher they have completed their work. The teacher then says, "Show me your boards" when most of the class is ready.

*What are some of the benefits of a personal white board?*

- The teacher can respond quickly to gaps in student understandings and skills. "Let's do some of these on our personal white boards until we have more mastery."

- Students can erase quickly so that they do not have to suffer the evidence of their mistake.

- They are motivating. Students love both the drill and thrill capability and the chance to do story problems with an engaging medium.

- Checking work gives the teacher instant feedback about student understanding.

*What is the benefit of this personal white board over a commercially purchased dry erase board?*

- It is much less expensive.

- Templates such as place value charts, number bond mats, hundreds boards, and number lines can be stored between the two pieces of tag board for easy access and reuse.

- Worksheets, story problems, and other problem sets can be done without marking the paper so that students can work on the problems independently at another time.

- Strips with story problems, number lines, and arrays can be inserted so students will still have a full piece of paper on which to write.

- The red versus white side distinction clarifies expectations. When working collaboratively, there is no need to use the red side. When working independently, students know how to keep their work private.

- The tag board can be removed if necessary to project the work.

# Scaffolds[4]

The scaffolds integrated into *A Story of Units*® give alternatives for how students access information as well as express and demonstrate their learning. Strategically placed margin notes are provided within each lesson, elaborating on the use of specific scaffolds at applicable times. They address many needs presented by English language learners, students with disabilities, students performing above grade level, and students performing below grade level. Many of the suggestions are organized by Universal Design for Learning (UDL) principles and are applicable to more than one population. To read more about the approach to differentiated instruction in *A Story of Units,* please refer to "How to Implement *A Story of Units.*"

---

[4]Students with disabilities may require Braille, large print, audio, or special digital files. Please visit the website www.p12.nysed.gov/specialed/aim for specific information on how to obtain student materials that satisfy the National Instructional Materials Accessibility Standard (NIMAS) format.

# Preparing to Teach a Module

Preparation of lessons will be more effective and efficient if there has been an adequate analysis of the module first. Each module in *A Story of Units*® can be compared to a chapter in a book. How is the module moving the plot, the mathematics, forward? What new learning is taking place? How are the topics and objectives building on one another? The following is a suggested process for preparing to teach a module.

Step 1: Get a preview of the plot.

A:   Read the Table of Contents. At a high level, what is the plot of the module? How does the story develop across the topics?

B:   Preview the module's Exit Tickets[5] to see the trajectory of the module's mathematics and the nature of the work students are expected to be able to do.

Note: When studying a PDF file, enter "Exit Ticket" into the search feature to navigate from one Exit Ticket to the next.

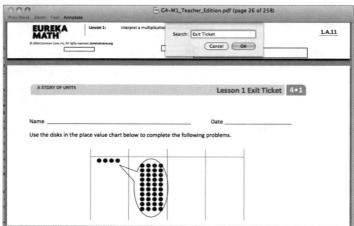

Step 2: Dig into the details.

A:   Dig into a careful reading of the Module Overview. While reading the narrative, *liberally* reference the lessons and Topic Overviews to clarify the meaning of the text—the lessons demonstrate the strategies, show how to use the models, clarify vocabulary, and build understanding of concepts. Consider searching the video gallery on *Eureka Math's* website to watch demonstrations of the use of models and other teaching techniques.

B:   Having thoroughly investigated the Module Overview, read through the chart entitled Overview of Module Topics and Lesson Objectives to further discern the plot of the module. How do the topics flow and tell a coherent story? How do the objectives move from simple to complex?

Step 3: Summarize the story.

Complete the Mid- and End-of-Module Assessments. Use the strategies and models presented in the module to explain the thinking involved. Again, liberally reference the work done in the lessons to see how students who are learning with the curriculum might respond.

---

[5]A more in-depth preview can be done by searching the Problem Sets rather than the Exit Tickets. Furthermore, this same process can be used to preview the coherence or flow of any component of the curriculum, such as Fluency Practice or Application Problems.

# Preparing to Teach a Lesson

A three-step process is suggested to prepare a lesson. It is understood that at times teachers may need to make adjustments (customizations) to lessons to fit the time constraints and unique needs of their students. The recommended planning process is outlined below. Note: The ladder of Step 2 is a metaphor for the teaching sequence. The sequence can be seen not only at the macro level in the role that this lesson plays in the overall story, but also at the lesson level, where each rung in the ladder represents the next step in understanding or the next skill needed to reach the objective. To reach the objective, or the top of the ladder, all students must be able to access the first rung and each successive rung.

Step 1: Discern the plot.

A: Briefly review the Table of Contents for the module, recalling the overall story of the module and analyzing the role of this lesson in the module.

B: Read the Topic Overview of the lesson, and then review the Problem Set and Exit Ticket of each lesson of the topic.

C: Review the assessment following the topic, keeping in mind that assessments can be found midway through the module and at the end of the module.

Step 2: Find the ladder.

A: Complete the lesson's Problem Set.

B: Analyze and write notes on the new complexities of each problem as well as the sequences and progressions throughout problems (e.g., pictorial to abstract, smaller to larger numbers, single- to multi-step problems). The new complexities are the rungs of the ladder.

C: Anticipate where students might struggle, and write a note about the potential cause of the struggle.

D: Answer the Student Debrief questions, always anticipating how students will respond.

Step 3: Hone the lesson.

At times, the lesson and Problem Set are appropriate for all students and the day's schedule. At others, they may need customizing. If the decision is to customize based on either the needs of students or scheduling constraints, a suggestion is to decide upon and designate "Must Do" and "Could Do" problems.

A: Select "Must Do" problems from the Problem Set that meet the objective and provide a coherent experience for students; reference the ladder. The expectation is that the majority of the class will complete the "Must Do" problems within the allocated time. While choosing the "Must Do" problems, keep in mind the need for a balance of calculations, various word problem types[6], and work at both the pictorial and abstract levels.

---

[6]See the Progression Documents "K, Counting and Cardinality" and "K–5, Operations and Algebraic Thinking" pp. 9 and 23, respectively.

B: "Must Do" problems might also include remedial work as necessary for the whole class, a small group, or individual students. Depending on anticipated difficulties, those problems might take different forms as shown in the chart below.

| Anticipated Difficulty | "Must Do" Remedial Problem Suggestion |
|---|---|
| The first problem of the Problem Set is too challenging. | Write a short sequence of problems on the board that provides a ladder to Problem 1. Direct the class or small group to complete those first problems to empower them to begin the Problem Set. Consider labeling these problems "Zero Problems" since they are done prior to Problem 1. |
| There is too big of a jump in complexity between two problems. | Provide a problem or set of problems that creates a bridge between the two problems. Label them with the number of the problem they follow. For example, if the challenging jump is between Problems 2 and 3, consider labeling these problems "Extra 2s." |
| Students lack fluency or foundational skills necessary for the lesson. | Before beginning the Problem Set, do a quick, engaging fluency exercise, such as a Rapid White Board Exchange, "Thrilling Drill," or Sprint. Before beginning any fluency activity for the first time, assess that students are poised for success with the easiest problem in the set. |
| More work is needed at the concrete or pictorial level. | Provide manipulatives or the opportunity to draw solution strategies. Especially in Kindergarten, at times the Problem Set or pencil and paper aspect might be completely excluded, allowing students to simply work with materials. |
| More work is needed at the abstract level. | Hone the Problem Set to reduce the amount of drawing as appropriate for certain students or the whole class. |

C: "Could Do" problems are for students who work with greater fluency and understanding and can, therefore, complete more work within a given time frame. Adjust the Exit Ticket and Homework to reflect the "Must Do" problems or to address scheduling constraints.

D: At times, a particularly tricky problem might be designated as a "Challenge!" problem. This can be motivating, especially for advanced students. Consider creating the opportunity for students to share their "Challenge!" solutions with the class at a weekly session or on video.

E: Consider how to best use the vignettes of the Concept Development section of the lesson. Read through the vignettes, and highlight selected parts to be included in the delivery of instruction so that students can be independently successful on the assigned task.

F: Pay close attention to the questions chosen for the Student Debrief. Regularly ask students, "What was the lesson's learning goal today?" Hone the goal with them.

# Assessment Summary

| Type | Administered | Format | Standards Addressed |
|---|---|---|---|
| Mid-Module Assessment Task | After Topic C | Constructed response with rubric | 5.NBT.1<br>5.NBT.2<br>5.NBT.3<br>5.NBT.4<br>5.MD.1 |
| End-of-Module Assessment Task | After Topic F | Constructed response with rubric | 5.NBT.1<br>5.NBT.2<br>5.NBT.3<br>5.NBT.4<br>5.NBT.7<br>5.MD.1 |

# Mathematics Curriculum

**5**
GRADE

## Topic A

# Multiplicative Patterns on the Place Value Chart

**5.NBT.1, 5.NBT.2, 5.MD.1**

| Focus Standards: | 5.NBT.1 | Recognize that in a multi-digit number, a digit in one place represents 10 times as much as it represents in the place to its right and 1/10 of what it represents in the place to its left. |
| --- | --- | --- |
| | 5.NBT.2 | Explain patterns in the number of zeros of the product when multiplying a number by powers of 10, and explain patterns in the placement of the decimal point when a decimal is multiplied or divided by a power of 10. Use whole-number exponents to denote powers of 10. |
| | 5.MD.1 | Convert among different-sized standard measurement units within a given measurement system (e.g., convert 5 cm to 0.05 m), and use these conversions in solving multi-step, real world problems. |
| **Instructional Days:** | 4 | |
| **Coherence** -Links from: | G4–M1 | Place Value, Rounding, and Algorithms for Addition and Subtraction |
| -Links to: | G6–M2 | Arithmetic Operations Including Dividing by a Fraction |

Topic A begins with a conceptual exploration of the multiplicative patterns of the base ten system. This exploration extends the place value work done with multi-digit whole numbers in Grade 4 to larger multi-digit whole numbers and decimals. Students use place value disks and a place value chart to build the place value chart from millions to thousandths. They compose and decompose units crossing the decimal with a view toward extending their knowledge of the *10 times as large* and *1/10 as large* relationships among whole number places to that of adjacent decimal places. This concrete experience is linked to the effects on the product when multiplying any number by a power of ten. For example, students notice that multiplying 0.4 by 1,000 shifts the position of the digits to the left three places, changing the digits' relationships to the decimal point and producing a product with a value that is $10 \times 10 \times 10$ as large (400.0) (**5.NBT.2**). Students explain these changes in value and shifts in position in terms of place value. Additionally, students learn a new and more efficient way to represent place value units using exponents (e.g., 1 thousand = 1,000 = $10^3$) (**5.NBT.2**). Conversions among metric units such as kilometers, meters, and centimeters give students an opportunity to apply these extended place value relationships and exponents in a meaningful context by exploring word problems in the last lesson of Topic A (**5.MD.1**).

**A Teaching Sequence Toward Mastery of Multiplicative Patterns on the Place Value Chart**

Objective 1:  Reason concretely and pictorially using place value understanding to relate adjacent base ten units from millions to thousandths.
(Lesson 1)

Objective 2:  Reason abstractly using place value understanding to relate adjacent base ten units from millions to thousandths.
(Lesson 2)

Objective 3:  Use exponents to name place value units, and explain patterns in the placement of the decimal point.
(Lesson 3)

Objective 4:  Use exponents to denote powers of 10 with application to metric conversions.
(Lesson 4)

# Lesson 1

Objective:  Reason concretely and pictorially using place value understanding to relate adjacent base ten units from millions to thousandths.

## Suggested Lesson Structure

■ Fluency Practice          (12 minutes)
■ Application Problem        (8 minutes)
■ Concept Development        (30 minutes)
■ Student Debrief           (10 minutes)
   **Total Time**           **(60 minutes)**

## Fluency Practice  (12 minutes)

- Sprint:  Multiply by 10  **4.NBT.1**          (8 minutes)
- Rename the Units—Choral Response  **2.NBT.1**  (2 minutes)
- Decimal Place Value  **4.NF.5–6**            (2 minutes)

### Sprint:  Multiply by 10  (8 minutes)

Materials:    (S) Multiply by 10 Sprint

Note:  Reviewing this fluency activity will acclimate students to the Sprint routine, a vital component of the fluency program.

Please see Directions for Administration of Sprints in the Module Overview for tips on implementation.

### Rename the Units—Choral Response  (2 minutes)

Notes:  This fluency activity reviews foundations that lead into today's lesson.

T:    (Write 10 ones = _____ ten.) Say the number sentence.
S:    10 ones = 1 ten.
T:    (Write 20 ones = _____ tens.) Say the number sentence.
S:    20 ones = 2 tens.

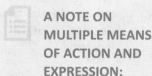

A NOTE ON
MULTIPLE MEANS
OF ACTION AND
EXPRESSION:

Throughout *A Story of Units*®, place value language is key. In earlier grades, teachers use units to refer to a number such as 245, as two *hundred* forty-five. Likewise, in Grades 4 and 5, decimals should be read emphasizing their unit form. For example, 0.2 would be read 2 *tenths* rather than *zero point two*. This emphasis on unit language not only strengthens student place value understanding, but it also builds important parallels between whole number and decimal fraction understanding.

NOTES ON
FLUENCY PRACTICE:

Think of fluency as having three goals:

- Maintenance (staying sharp on previously learned skills).

- Preparation (targeted practice for the current lesson).

- Anticipation (skills that ensure that students will be ready for the in-depth work of upcoming lessons).

Lesson 1:        Reason concretely and pictorially using place value understanding to
                              relate adjacent base ten units from millions to thousandths.

T:    30 ones.

S:    3 tens.

Repeat the process for 80 ones, 90 ones, 100 ones, 110 ones, 120 ones, 170, 270, 670, 640, and 830.

## Decimal Place Value  (2 minutes)

Materials:    (S) Personal white board, unlabeled hundreds to hundredths place value chart (Template 1)

Note:  Reviewing this Grade 4 topic lays a foundation for students to better understand place value to bigger and smaller units.

T:    (Project unlabeled hundreds to hundredths place value chart. Draw 3 ten disks in the tens column.) How many tens do you see?

S:    3 tens.

T:    (Write 3 underneath the disks.) There are 3 tens and how many ones?

S:    Zero ones.

T:    (Write 0 in the ones column. Below it, write 3 tens = ____.) Fill in the blank.

S:    3 tens = 30.

Repeat the process for 3 tenths = 0.3.

T:    (Write 4 tenths = ____.) Show the answer in your place value chart.

S:    (Draw four 1 tenth disks. Below it, write 0.4.)

Repeat the process for 3 hundredths, 43 hundredths, 5 hundredths, 35 hundredths, 7 ones 35 hundredths, 9 ones 24 hundredths, and 6 tens 2 ones 4 hundredths.

Note:  Place value disks are used as models throughout the curriculum and can be represented in two different ways. A disk with a value labeled inside of it (above) should be drawn or placed on a place value chart with no headings. The value of the disk in its appropriate column indicates the column heading. A place value disk drawn as a dot should be used on place value charts *with* headings, as shown in Problem 1 of Concept Development. The dot is a faster way to represent the place value disk and is used as students move further away from a concrete stage of learning.

## Application Problem  (8 minutes)

Farmer Jim keeps 12 hens in every coop. If Farmer Jim has 20 coops, how many hens does he have in all? If every hen lays 9 eggs on Monday, how many eggs will Farmer Jim collect on Monday? Explain your reasoning using words, numbers, or pictures.

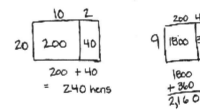

Note:  This problem is intended to activate prior knowledge from Grade 4 and offer a successful start to Grade 5. Some students may use area models to solve, while others may choose to use the standard algorithm. Still others may draw tape diagrams to show their thinking. Allow students to share work and compare approaches.

© 2015 Great Minds. eureka-math.org
G5-M1-TE-B1-1.3.1-1.2016

## Concept Development  (30 minutes)

**Materials:**    (S) Millions through thousandths place value chart (Template 2), personal white board

The place value chart and its *times 10* relationships are familiar territory for students. New learning in Grade 5 focuses on understanding a new fractional unit of *thousandths* as well as the decomposition of larger units to those that are 1 tenth as large. Building the place value chart from right (tenths) to left (millions) before beginning the following problem sequence may be advisable. Encourage students to multiply and then bundle to form the next largest place (e.g., 10 × 1 hundred = 10 hundreds, which can be bundled to form 1 thousand).

**Problem 1:  Divide single units by 10 to build the place value chart to introduce thousandths.**

T:  Slide your millions through thousandths place value chart into your personal white board. Show 1 million, using disks, on the place value chart.

S:  (Work.)

T:  How can we show 1 million using hundred thousands? Work with your partner to show this on your chart.

S:  1 million is the same as 10 hundred thousands.

T:  What is the result if I divide 10 hundred thousands by 10? Talk with your partner, and use your chart to find the quotient.

T:  (Circulate.) I saw that David put 10 disks in the hundred thousands place and then distributed them into 10 equal groups. How many are in each group?

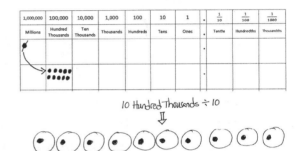

S:  When I divide 10 hundred thousands by 10, I get 1 hundred thousand in each group.

T:  Let me record what I hear you saying. (Record on class board.)

*10 hundred thousands ÷ 10 = 1 hundred thousand*          *1 million ÷ 10 = 1 hundred thousand*

*1 hundred thousand is $\frac{1}{10}$ as large as 1 million.*

| Millions | Hundred Thousands | Ten Thousands | Thousands | Hundreds | Tens | Ones | Tenths | Hundredths | Thousandths |
|---|---|---|---|---|---|---|---|---|---|
| 1÷10 |  |  |  |  |  |  |  |  |  |
|  | 1 |  |  |  |  |  |  |  |  |

T:  Draw 1 hundred thousands disk on your chart. What is the result if we divide 1 hundred thousand by 10? Show this on your chart and write a division sentence.

**Lesson 1:**     Reason concretely and pictorially using place value understanding to relate adjacent base ten units from millions to thousandths.

**EUREKA MATH**

Continue this sequence until the hundredths place is reached, emphasizing the unbundling for 10 of the smaller unit and then the division. Record the place values and equations (using unit form) on the board being careful to point out the *1 tenth as large* relationship:

> 1 million ÷ 10 = 1 hundred thousand
>
> 1 hundred thousand ÷ 10 = 1 ten thousand
>
> 1 ten thousand ÷ 10 = 1 thousand
>
> 1 thousand ÷ 10 = 1 hundred

(Continue through 1 tenth ÷ 10 = 1 hundredth.)

**NOTES ON
MULTIPLE MEANS
OF ENGAGEMENT:**

Students who have limited experience with decimal fractions may be supported by a return to Grade 4's Module 6 to review decimal place value and symmetry with respect to the ones place.

Conversely, student understanding of decimal fraction place value units may be extended by asking for predictions of units one-tenth as large as the thousandths place and those beyond.

**MP.8**

T:  What patterns do you notice in the way the units are named in our place value system?

S:  The ones place is the middle. There are tens on the left and tenths on the right, hundreds on the left and hundredths on the right.

T:  (Point to the chart.) Using this pattern, can you predict what the name of the unit that is to the right of the hundredths place (1 tenth as large as hundredths) might be?

S:  (Share. Label the thousandths place.)

T:  Think about the pattern that we've seen with other adjacent places. Talk with your partner and predict how we might show 1 hundredth using thousandths disks. Show this on your chart.

S:  Just like all the other places, it takes 10 of the smaller unit to make 1 of the larger, so it will take 10 thousandths to make 1 hundredth.

T:  Use your chart to show the result if we divide 1 hundredth by 10, and write the division sentence.

S:  (Share.)

T:  (Add this equation to the others on the board.)

**NOTES ON
MULTIPLE MEANS
OF ENGAGEMENT:**

Proportional materials such as base ten blocks can help English language learners distinguish between place value labels like *hundredth* and *thousandth* more easily by offering clues to their relative sizes. These students can be encouraged to name the units in their first language and then compare them to their English counterparts. Sometimes the roots of these number words are very similar. These parallels enrich the experience and understanding of all students.

**Problem 2:  Multiply copies of one unit by 10, 100, and 1,000.**

> 0.4 × 10
>
> 0.04 × 10
>
> 0.004 × 10

T:  Use digits to represent 4 tenths at the top of your place value chart.

S:  (Write.)

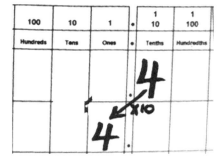

Lesson 1:     Reason concretely and pictorially using place value understanding to relate adjacent base ten units from millions to thousandths.                    21

© 2015 Great Minds. eureka-math.org
G5-M1-TE-B1-1.3.1-1.2016

T: Work with your partner to find the value of 10 times 0.4. Show your result at the bottom of your place value chart.

S: 4 tenths × 10 = 40 tenths, which is the same as 4 wholes. → 4 ones is 10 times as large as 4 tenths.

T: On your place value chart, use arrows to show how the value of the digits has changed. (On the place value chart, draw an arrow to indicate the shift of the digit to the left, and write × 10 near the arrow.)

T: Why does the digit move one place to the left?

S: Because it is 10 times as large, it has to be bundled for the next larger unit.

Repeat with 0.04 × 10 and 0.004 × 1,000. Use unit form to state each problem, and encourage students to articulate how the value of the digit changes and why it changes position in the chart.

**Problem 3: Divide copies of one unit by 10, 100, and 1,000.**

6 ÷ 10

6 ÷ 100

6 ÷ 1,000

Follow a similar sequence to guide students in articulating changes in value and shifts in position while showing it on the place value chart.

Repeat with 0.7 ÷ 10, 0.7 ÷ 100, and 0.05 ÷ 10.

**Problem 4: Multiply mixed units by 10, 100, and 1,000.**

2.43 × 10

2.43 × 100

2.43 × 1,000

T: Write the digits two and forty-three hundredths on your place value chart, and multiply by 10, then 100, and then 1,000. Compare these products with your partner.

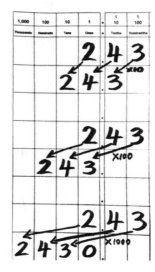

Lead students to discuss how the digits shift as a result of their change in value by isolating one digit, such as the 3, and comparing its value in each product.

**Problem 5**

745 ÷ 10

745 ÷ 100

745 ÷ 1,000

Engage in a similar discussion regarding the shift and change in value for a digit in these division problems. See discussion above.

Lesson 1:     Reason concretely and pictorially using place value understanding to relate adjacent base ten units from millions to thousandths.

EUREKA MATH

## Problem Set  (10 minutes)

Students should do their personal best to complete the Problem Set within the allotted 10 minutes. Some problems do not specify a method for solving. This is an intentional reduction of scaffolding that invokes MP.5, Use Appropriate Tools Strategically. Students should solve these problems using the RDW approach used for Application Problems.

For some classes, it may be appropriate to modify the assignment by specifying which problems students should work on first. With this option, let the purposeful sequencing of the Problem Set guide the selections so that problems continue to be scaffolded. Balance word problems with other problem types to ensure a range of practice. Consider assigning incomplete problems for homework or at another time during the day.

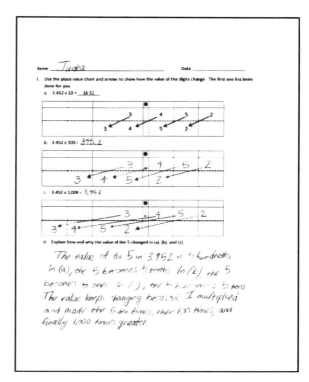

## Student Debrief  (10 minutes)

**Lesson Objective:**  Reason concretely and pictorially using place value understanding to relate adjacent base ten units from millions to thousandths.

The Student Debrief is intended to invite reflection and active processing of the total lesson experience.

Invite students to review their solutions for the Problem Set. They should check work by comparing answers with a partner before going over answers as a class. Look for misconceptions or misunderstandings that can be addressed in the Debrief. Guide students in a conversation to debrief the Problem Set and process the lesson.

Any combination of the questions below may be used to lead the discussion.

- Compare the solutions you found when multiplying by 10 and dividing by 10 (3.452 × 10 and 345 ÷ 10). How do the solutions of these two expressions relate to the value of the original quantity? How do they relate to each other?

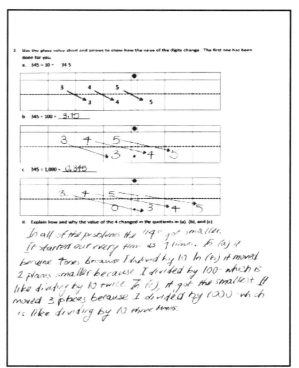

Lesson 1:      Reason concretely and pictorially using place value understanding to          23
               relate adjacent base ten units from millions to thousandths.

© 2015 Great Minds. eureka-math.org
G5-M1-TE-B1-1.3.1-1.2016

- What do you notice about the number of zeros in your products when multiplying by 10, 100, and 1,000 relative to the number of places the digits shift on the place value chart? What patterns do you notice?

- What is the same and what is different about the products for Problems 1(a), 1(b), and 1(c)? (Encourage students to notice that the digits are exactly the same. Only the values have changed.)

- When solving Problem 2(c), many of you noticed the use of our new place value. (Lead a brief class discussion to reinforce what value this place represents. Reiterate the symmetry of the places on either side of the ones place and the size of *thousandths* relative to other place values like tenths and ones.)

## Exit Ticket (3 minutes)

After the Student Debrief, instruct students to complete the Exit Ticket. A review of their work will help with assessing students' understanding of the concepts that were presented in today's lesson and planning more effectively for future lessons. The questions may be read aloud to the students.

Lesson 1:      Reason concretely and pictorially using place value understanding to relate adjacent base ten units from millions to thousandths.

EUREKA MATH

© 2015 Great Minds. eureka-math.org
G5-M1-TE-B1-1.3.1-1.2016

# A

Number Correct: _____

Multiply by 10

| | | |
|---|---|---|
| 1. | 12 × 10 = | |
| 2. | 14 × 10 = | |
| 3. | 15 × 10 = | |
| 4. | 17 × 10 = | |
| 5. | 81 × 10 = | |
| 6. | 10 × 81 = | |
| 7. | 21 × 10 = | |
| 8. | 22 × 10 = | |
| 9. | 23 × 10 = | |
| 10. | 29 × 10 = | |
| 11. | 92 × 10 = | |
| 12. | 10 × 92 = | |
| 13. | 18 × 10 = | |
| 14. | 19 × 10 = | |
| 15. | 20 × 10 = | |
| 16. | 30 × 10 = | |
| 17. | 40 × 10 = | |
| 18. | 80 × 10 = | |
| 19. | 10 × 80 = | |
| 20. | 10 × 50 = | |
| 21. | 10 × 90 = | |
| 22. | 10 × 70 = | |

| | | |
|---|---|---|
| 23. | 34 × 10 = | |
| 24. | 134 × 10 = | |
| 25. | 234 × 10 = | |
| 26. | 334 × 10 = | |
| 27. | 834 × 10 = | |
| 28. | 10 × 834 = | |
| 29. | 45 × 10 = | |
| 30. | 145 × 10 = | |
| 31. | 245 × 10 = | |
| 32. | 345 × 10 = | |
| 33. | 945 × 10 = | |
| 34. | 56 × 10 = | |
| 35. | 456 × 10 = | |
| 36. | 556 × 10 = | |
| 37. | 950 × 10 = | |
| 38. | 10 × 950 = | |
| 39. | 16 × 10 = | |
| 40. | 10 × 60 = | |
| 41. | 493 × 10 = | |
| 42. | 10 × 84 = | |
| 43. | 96 × 10 = | |
| 44. | 10 × 580 = | |

Lesson 1:    Reason concretely and pictorially using place value understanding to relate adjacent base ten units from millions to thousandths.

25

# B

Number Correct: _____

Improvement: _____

Multiply by 10

| | | |
|---|---|---|
| 1. | 13 × 10 = | |
| 2. | 14 × 10 = | |
| 3. | 15 × 10 = | |
| 4. | 19 × 10 = | |
| 5. | 91 × 10 = | |
| 6. | 10 × 91 = | |
| 7. | 31 × 10 = | |
| 8. | 32 × 10 = | |
| 9. | 33 × 10 = | |
| 10. | 38 × 10 = | |
| 11. | 83 × 10 = | |
| 12. | 10 × 83 = | |
| 13. | 28 × 10 = | |
| 14. | 29 × 10 = | |
| 15. | 30 × 10 = | |
| 16. | 40 × 10 = | |
| 17. | 50 × 10 = | |
| 18. | 90 × 10 = | |
| 19. | 10 × 90 = | |
| 20. | 10 × 20 = | |
| 21. | 10 × 60 = | |
| 22. | 10 × 80 = | |

| | | |
|---|---|---|
| 23. | 43 × 10 = | |
| 24. | 143 × 10 = | |
| 25. | 243 × 10 = | |
| 26. | 343 × 10 = | |
| 27. | 743 × 10 = | |
| 28. | 10 × 743 = | |
| 29. | 54 × 10 = | |
| 30. | 154 × 10 = | |
| 31. | 254 × 10 = | |
| 32. | 354 × 10 = | |
| 33. | 854 × 10 = | |
| 34. | 65 × 10 = | |
| 35. | 465 × 10 = | |
| 36. | 565 × 10 = | |
| 37. | 960 × 10 = | |
| 38. | 10 × 960 = | |
| 39. | 17 × 10 = | |
| 40. | 10 × 70 = | |
| 41. | 582 × 10 = | |
| 42. | 10 × 73 = | |
| 43. | 98 × 10 = | |
| 44. | 10 × 470 = | |

Lesson 1: Reason concretely and pictorially using place value understanding to relate adjacent base ten units from millions to thousandths.

EUREKA MATH

Name _____     Date _____

1.  Use the place value chart and arrows to show how the value of the each digit changes. The first one has been done for you.

    a.  3.452 × 10 = ___34.52___

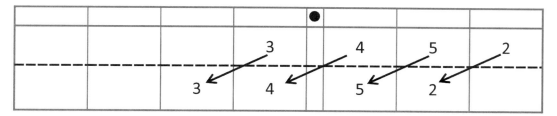

    b.  3.452 × 100 = _____

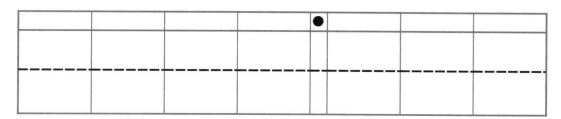

    c.  3.452 × 1,000 = _____

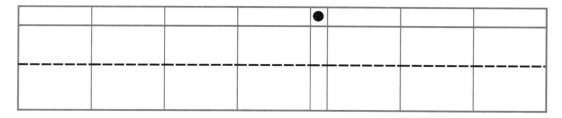

    d.  Explain how and why the value of the 5 changed in (a), (b), and (c).

EUREKA MATH      Lesson 1:      Reason concretely and pictorially using place value understanding to          27
                                 relate adjacent base ten units from millions to thousandths.

                                 © 2015 Great Minds. eureka-math.org
                                 G5-M1-TE-B1-1.3.1-1.2016

2. Use the place value chart and arrows to show how the value of each digit changes. The first one has been done for you.

   a.  345 ÷ 10 = ___34.5___

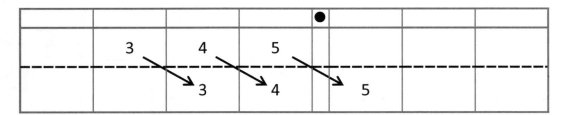

   b.  345 ÷ 100 = _____

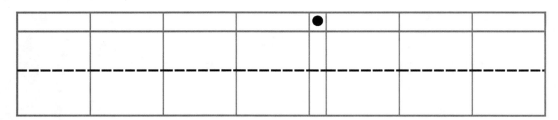

   c.  345 ÷ 1,000 =_____

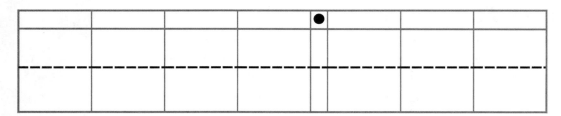

   d.  Explain how and why the value of the 4 changed in the quotients in (a), (b), and (c).

**Lesson 1:**   Reason concretely and pictorially using place value understanding to relate adjacent base ten units from millions to thousandths.

**EUREKA MATH**

3. A manufacturer made 7,234 boxes of coffee stirrers. Each box contains 1,000 stirrers. How many stirrers did they make? Explain your thinking, and include a statement of the solution.

4. A student used his place value chart to show a number. After the teacher instructed him to multiply his number by 10, the chart showed 3,200.4. Draw a picture of what the place value chart looked like at first.

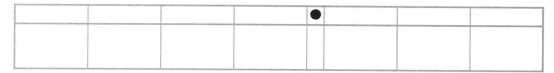

Explain how you decided what to draw on your place value chart. Be sure to include your reasoning about how the value of each digit was affected by the multiplication. Use words, pictures, or numbers.

5. A microscope has a setting that magnifies an object so that it appears 100 times as large when viewed through the eyepiece. If a tiny insect is 0.095 cm long, how long will the insect appear in centimeters through the microscope? Explain how you know.

Lesson 1: Reason concretely and pictorially using place value understanding to relate adjacent base ten units from millions to thousandths.

Name _____     Date _____

Use the place value chart and arrows to show how the value of each digit changes.

a.   6.671 × 100 = _____

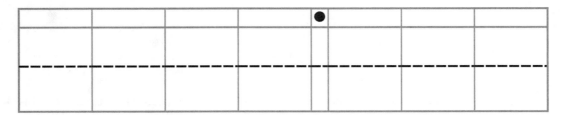

b.   684 ÷ 1,000 = _____

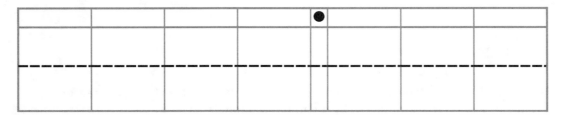

**Lesson 1:**          Reason concretely and pictorially using place value understanding to
                                            relate adjacent base ten units from millions to thousandths.

© 2015 Great Minds. eureka-math.org
G5-M1-TE-B1-1.3.1-1.2016

**EUREKA
MATH**

Name _____   Date _____

1. Use the place value chart and arrows to show how the value of each digit changes. The first one has been done for you.

    a.   4.582 × 10 = ____45.82____

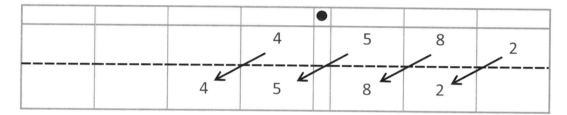

    b.   7.281 × 100 = _____

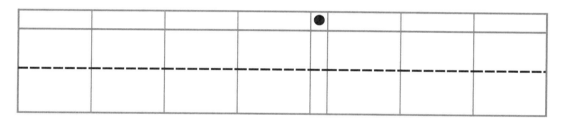

    c.   9.254 × 1,000 = _____

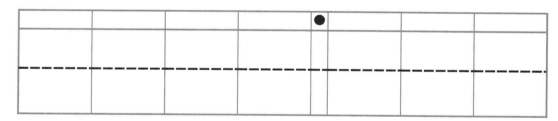

    d.   Explain how and why the value of the 2 changed in (a), (b), and (c).

EUREKA MATH

Lesson 1:   Reason concretely and pictorially using place value understanding to relate adjacent base ten units from millions to thousandths.

31

© 2015 Great Minds. eureka-math.org
G5-M1-TE-B1-1.3.1-1.2016

2. Use the place value chart and arrows to show how the value of each digit changes. The first one has been done for you.

   a.   $2.46 \div 10 = $ ___0.246___

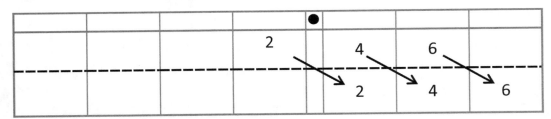

   b.   $678 \div 100 = $ _____

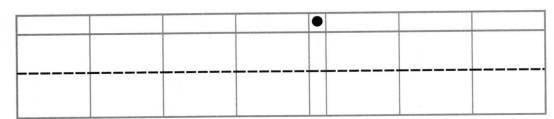

   c.   $67 \div 1,000 = $ _____

   d.   Explain how and why the value of the 6 changed in the quotients in (a), (b), and (c).

Lesson 1:   Reason concretely and pictorially using place value understanding to relate adjacent base ten units from millions to thousandths.

EUREKA
MATH

3.  Researchers counted 8,912 monarch butterflies on one branch of a tree at a site in Mexico. They estimated that the total number of butterflies at the site was 1,000 times as large. About how many butterflies were at the site in all? Explain your thinking, and include a statement of the solution.

4.  A student used his place value chart to show a number. After the teacher instructed him to divide his number by 100, the chart showed 28.003. Draw a picture of what the place value chart looked like at first.

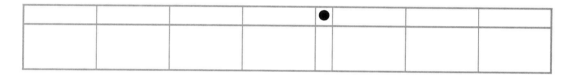

    Explain how you decided what to draw on your place value chart. Be sure to include reasoning about how the value of each digit was affected by the division.

5.  On a map, the perimeter of a park is 0.251 meters. The actual perimeter of the park is 1,000 times as large. What is the actual perimeter of the park? Explain how you know using a place value chart.

unlabeled hundreds through hundredths place value chart

**Lesson 1:** Reason concretely and pictorially using place value understanding to relate adjacent base ten units from millions to thousandths.

© 2015 Great Minds. eureka-math.org
G5-M1-TE-B1-1.3.1-1.2016

EUREKA
MATH

| 1,000,000 | 100,000 | 10,000 | 1,000 | 100 | 10 | 1 | . | $\frac{1}{10}$ | $\frac{1}{100}$ | $\frac{1}{1000}$ |
|---|---|---|---|---|---|---|---|---|---|---|
| Millions | Hundred Thousands | Ten Thousands | Thousands | Hundreds | Tens | Ones | . | Tenths | Hundredths | Thousandths |
| | | | | | | | . | | | |
| | | | | | | | . | | | |
| | | | | | | | . | | | |
| | | | | | | | | | | |
| | | | | | | | | | | |
| | | | | | | | | | | |
| | | | | | | | | | | |
| | | | | | | | | | | |
| | | | | | | | | | | |
| | | | | | | | | | | |

millions through thousandths place value chart

Lesson 1:   Reason concretely and pictorially using place value understanding to relate adjacent base ten units from millions to thousandths.

35

# Lesson 2

Objective: Reason abstractly using place value understanding to relate adjacent base ten units from millions to thousandths.

## Suggested Lesson Structure

■ Fluency Practice          (12 minutes)
■ Application Problem        (10 minutes)
■ Concept Development        (28 minutes)
■ Student Debrief           (10 minutes)

**Total Time**              **(60 minutes)**

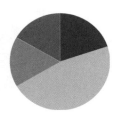

A NOTE ON
STANDARDS
ALIGNMENT:

Fluency tasks are included not only as warm-ups for the current lesson, but also as opportunities to retain past number understandings and to sharpen those understandings needed for coming work. Skip-counting in Grade 5 provides support for the common multiple work covered in Module 3.

Additionally, returning to a familiar and well-understood fluency can provide a student with a feeling of success before tackling a new body of work.

Consider including body movements to accompany skip-counting exercises (e.g., jumping jacks, toe touches, arm stretches, or dance movements like the *Macarena*).

## Fluency Practice  (12 minutes)

▪ Skip-Counting  **3.OA.4–6**                        (3 minutes)
▪ Take Out the Tens  **2.NBT.1**                      (2 minutes)
▪ Bundle Ten and Change Units  **4.NBT.1**   (2 minutes)
▪ Multiply and Divide by 10  **5.NBT.1**        (5 minutes)

## Skip-Counting  (3 minutes)

Note:  Practicing skip-counting on the number line builds a foundation for accessing higher order concepts throughout the year.

Direct students to count forward and backward by threes to 36, emphasizing the transitions of crossing the ten. Direct students to count forward and backward by fours to 48, emphasizing the transitions of crossing the ten.

## Take Out the Tens  (2 minutes)

Materials:   (S) Personal white board

Note:  Decomposing whole numbers into different units lays a foundation to do the same with decimal fractions.

    T:   (Write 83 ones = _____ tens _____ ones.) Write the number sentence.
    S:   (Write 83 ones = 8 tens 3 ones.)

Repeat the process for 93 ones, 103 ones, 113 ones, 163 ones, 263 ones, 463 ones, and 875 ones.

## Bundle Ten and Change Units  (2 minutes)

Note:  Reviewing this fluency area helps students work toward mastery of changing place value units in the base ten system.

  T:  (Write 10 hundreds = 1 _____.) Say the number sentence, filling in the blank.
  S:  10 hundreds = 1 thousand.

Repeat the process for 10 tens = 1 _____, 10 ones = 1 _____, 10 tenths = 1 _____, 10 thousandths = 1 _____, and 10 hundredths = 1 _____.

## Multiply and Divide by 10  (5 minutes)

Materials:  (T) Millions through thousandth place value chart (Lesson 1 Template) (S) Personal white board, millions through thousandths place value chart (Lesson 1 Template)

Note:  Reviewing this skill from Lesson 1 helps students work toward mastery.

  T:  (Project the place value chart from millions to thousandths.) Draw three ones disks, and write the total value of the disks below it.
  S:  (Draw three disks in the ones column. Below it, write 3.)
  T:  Multiply by 10. Cross out each disk and the number 3 to show that you're changing its value.
  S:  (Cross out each disk in the ones column and the 3. Draw arrows to the tens column, and draw three disks in the tens column. Below it, write 3 in the tens column and 0 in the ones column.)

Repeat the process for 2 hundredths, 3 tenths 2 hundredths, 3 tenths 2 hundredths 4 thousandths, 2 tenths 4 hundredths 5 thousandths, and 1 tenth 3 thousandths. Repeat the process for dividing by 10 for this possible sequence: 2 ones, 3 tenths, 2 ones 3 tenths, 2 ones 3 tenths 5 hundredths, 5 tenths 2 hundredths, and 1 ten 5 thousandths.

## Application Problem  (10 minutes)

A school district ordered 247 boxes of pencils. Each box contains 100 pencils. If the pencils are to be shared evenly among 10 classrooms, how many pencils will each class receive? Draw a place value chart to show your thinking.

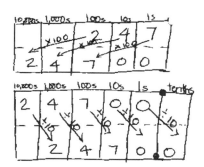

Each classroom receives 2,470 pencils.

A NOTE ON
APPLICATION
PROBLEMS:

Application Problems are designed to reach back to the learning in the prior day's lesson. Today's problem requires students to show thinking using the concrete–pictorial approach used in Lesson 1 to find the product and quotient. This will act as an anticipatory set for today's lesson.

EUREKA
MATH®

Lesson 2:    Reason abstractly using place value understanding to relate adjacent
             base ten units from millions to thousandths.                                      37

© 2015 Great Minds. eureka-math.org
G5-M1-TE-B1-1.3.1-1.2016

## Concept Development (28 minutes)

**Materials:** (S) Millions through thousandths place value chart (Lesson 1 Template), personal white board

T: Turn and share with your partner. What do you remember from yesterday's lesson about how adjacent units on the place value chart are related?

S: (Share.)

T: Moving one position to the left on the place value chart makes units 10 times larger. Conversely, moving one position to the right makes units 1 tenth the size.

As students move through the sequence of problems, encourage a move away from the concrete–pictorial representations of the products and quotients and, instead, move toward reasoning about the patterns of the number of zeros in the products and quotients and the placement of the decimal.

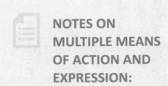

**NOTES ON MULTIPLE MEANS OF ACTION AND EXPRESSION:**

Although students are being encouraged toward more abstract reasoning in the lesson, it is important to keep concrete materials like place value charts and place value disks accessible to students while these place value relationships are being solidified. Giving students the freedom to move between levels of abstraction on a task-by-task basis can decrease anxiety when working with more difficult applications.

### Problem 1

$367 \times 10$

$367 \div 10$

$4,367 \times 10$

$4,367 \div 10$

T: Work with your partner to solve these problems. Write two complete number sentences on your board.

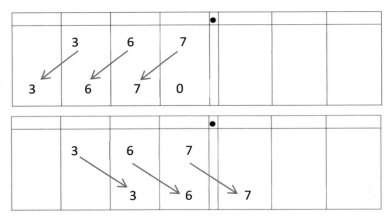

S: $367 \times 10 = 3,670.$ → $367 \div 10 = 36.7.$

---

     **Lesson 2:**    Reason abstractly using place value understanding to relate adjacent base ten units from millions to thousandths.

**EUREKA MATH**

**MP.3**

T: Explain how you got your answers. What are the similarities and differences between the two answers?

S: The digits are the same, but their values have changed. Their position in the number is different. → The 3 is 10 times larger in the product than in the factor. It was 3 hundreds. Now, it is 3 thousands. → The six started out as 6 tens, but once it was divided by 10, it is now 1 tenth as large because it is 6 ones.

T: What patterns do you notice in the number of zeros in the product and the placement of the decimal in the quotient? What do you notice about the number of zeros in your factors and the shift in places in your product? What do you notice about the number of zeros in your divisor and the shift in places in your quotient?

**MP.2**

S: (Share.)

Repeat this sequence with the last pair of expressions ($4{,}367 \times 10$ and $4{,}367 \div 10$). Encourage students to visualize the place value chart and attempt to find the product and quotient without drawing the chart. Circulate. Watch for misconceptions and students who are not ready to work on an abstract level. As students share thinking, encourage the use of the language *10 times as large* and *1 tenth as large.*

**Problem 2**

$215.6 \times 100$

$215.6 \div 100$

$3.7 \times 100$

$3.7 \div 100$

T: Now, solve with your partner by visualizing your place value chart and recording only your products and quotients. You may check your work using a place value chart. (Circulate. Look for students who may still need the support of the place value chart.)

S: (Solve.)

T: Compare your work with your partner's. Do you agree? How many times did the digits shift in each problem, and why? Share your thinking with your partner.

**MP.7**

S: The digits shifted two places to the left when we multiplied and two places to the right when we divided. → This time the digits each shifted two places because there are 2 zeros in 100. → The values of the products are 100 times as large, so the digits had to shift to larger units.

**Problem 3**

$0.482 \times 1{,}000$

$482 \div 1{,}000$

Follow a similar sequence for these expressions.

Lesson 2:      Reason abstractly using place value understanding to relate adjacent             39
                base ten units from millions to thousandths.

© 2015 Great Minds. eureka-math.org
G5-M1-TE-B1-1.3.1-1.2016

## Problem Set  (10 minutes)

Students should do their personal best to complete the Problem Set within the allotted 10 minutes. For some classes, it may be appropriate to modify the assignment by specifying which problems they work on first. Some problems do not specify a method for solving. Students solve these problems using the RDW approach used for Application Problems.

## Student Debrief  (10 minutes)

**Lesson Objective:** Reason abstractly using place value understanding to relate adjacent base ten units from millions to thousandths.

The Student Debrief is intended to invite reflection and active processing of the total lesson experience.

Invite students to review their solutions for the Problem Set. They should check work by comparing answers with a partner before going over answers as a class. Look for misconceptions or misunderstandings that can be addressed in the Debrief. Guide students in a conversation to debrief the Problem Set and process the lesson.

Any combination of the questions below may be used to lead the discussion.

- Compare and contrast answers in Problem 1(a) and (b) or 1(c) and (d).
- What is similar about the process you used to solve Problem 1(a), (c), (e), and (g)?
- What is similar about the process you used to solve Problem 1(b), (d), (f), and (h)?
- When asked to find the number 1 tenth as large as another number, what operation would you use? Explain how you know.
- When solving Problem 2, how did the number of zeros in the factors help you determine the product?

Name Tia _____ Date _____

1. Solve.
   a. 54,000 × 10 = _540,000_
   b. 54,000 ÷ 10 = _5,400_
   c. 8.7 × 10 = _87_
   d. 8.7 ÷ 10 = _0.87_
   e. 0.13 × 100 = _13_
   f. 13 ÷ 1,000 = _0.013_
   g. 3.12 × 1,000 = _3,120_
   h. 4031.2 ÷ 100 = _40.312_

2. Find the products.
   a. 19,340 × 10 = _193,400_
   b. 19,340 × 100 = _1,934,000_
   c. 19,340 × 1,000 = _19,340,000_
   d. Explain how you decided on the number of zeros in the products for (a), (b), and (c).

   I visualized the place value chart. Times 10 shifted the digits one place to the left, so I added the zeros to the end. Times 100, shifted the digits twice. I added 2 zeros. For times 1000, I added three digits.

   19,340 × 1 ten = 19,340 tens = 193,400
   19,340 × 1 hundred = 19,340 hundreds = 1,934,000
   19,340 × 1 thousand = 19,340 thousands = 19,340,000

3. Find the quotients.
   a. 152 ÷ 10 = _15.2_
   b. 152 ÷ 100 = _1.52_
   c. 152 ÷ 1,000 = _0.152_
   d. Explain how you decided where to place the decimal in the quotients in (a), (b), and (c).

   I visualized the place value chart. When dividing by any multiple of 10, the number of zeros tells you how many places the digits shift to the right. Dividing by 10, shifted the digits one place. Dividing by 100, shifted the digits two places. Dividing by 1000, shifted three places.

4. Janice thinks that 20 hundredths is equivalent to 2 thousandths because 20 hundreds is equal to 2 thousands. Use words and a place value chart to correct Janice's error.

   This place value chart showed that 20 hundreds = 2 thousands because they have the same value of 2,000. But 20 hundredths ≠ 2 thousandths, because they don't have the same value.

5. Canada has a population that is about $\frac{1}{10}$ as large as the United States. If Canada's population is about 32 million, about how many people live in the United States? Explain the number of zeros in your answer.

   1 unit = 32 millions
   10 units = 10 × 32 millions
            = 320 millions
            = 320,000,000

   About 320 millions people live in the U.S. Since 1 million has 6 zeros, 320 millions will also have 6 additional zeros at the end.

Lesson 2: Reason abstractly using place value understanding to relate adjacent base ten units from millions to thousandths.

**EUREKA MATH**

© 2015 Great Minds. eureka-math.org
G5-M1-TE-B1-1.3.1-1.2016

- Give an example of a time when there will be a different number of zeros in the factors and the product? (If students have difficulty answering, give them the example of 4 × 5, 4 × 50, 40 × 50. Then, ask students to give other examples.)

- When dividing by 10, what happens to the digits in the quotient? When multiplying by 100, what happens to the digits in the product?

- Be prepared for students to make mistakes when answering Problem 4. (Using a place value chart to solve this problem may reduce the errors. Encourage discussion about the relative size of the units in relation to a whole and why hundredths are larger than thousandths.)

## Exit Ticket  (3 minutes)

After the Student Debrief, instruct students to complete the Exit Ticket. A review of their work will help with assessing students' understanding of the concepts that were presented in today's lesson and planning more effectively for future lessons. The questions may be read aloud to the students.

Lesson 2:    Reason abstractly using place value understanding to relate adjacent
            base ten units from millions to thousandths.                                    41

© 2015 Great Minds. eureka-math.org
G5-M1-TE-B1-1.3.1-1.2016

Name _____     Date _____

1. Solve.

   a. 54,000 × 10 = _____

   b. 54,000 ÷ 10 = _____

   c. 8.7 × 10 = _____

   d. 8.7 ÷ 10 = _____

   e. 0.13 × 100 = _____

   f. 13 ÷ 1,000 = _____

   g. 3.12 × 1,000 = _____

   h. 4,031.2 ÷ 100 = _____

2. Find the products.

   a. 19,340 × 10 = _____

   b. 19,340 × 100 = _____

   c. 19,340 × 1,000 = _____

   d. Explain how you decided on the number of zeros in the products for (a), (b), and (c).

**Lesson 2:**   Reason abstractly using place value understanding to relate adjacent base ten units from millions to thousandths.

EUREKA MATH

3. Find the quotients.

   a. $152 \div 10 =$ _____

   b. $152 \div 100 =$ _____

   c. $152 \div 1,000 =$ _____

   d. Explain how you decided where to place the decimal in the quotients for (a), (b), and (c).

4. Janice thinks that 20 hundredths is equivalent to 2 thousandths because 20 hundreds is equal to 2 thousands. Use words and a place value chart to correct Janice's error.

5. Canada has a population that is about $\frac{1}{10}$ as large as the United States. If Canada's population is about 32 million, about how many people live in the United States? Explain the number of zeros in your the answer.

Lesson 2:    Reason abstractly using place value understanding to relate adjacent base ten units from millions to thousandths.

© 2015 Great Minds. eureka-math.org
G5-M1-TE-B1-1.3.1-1.2016

43

Name _____   Date _____

1. Solve.

   a.   $32.1 \times 10 =$ _____

   b.   $3632.1 \div 10 =$ _____

2. Solve.

   a.   $455 \times 1,000 =$ _____

   b.   $455 \div 1,000 =$ _____

**Lesson 2:**      Reason abstractly using place value understanding to relate adjacent
base ten units from millions to thousandths.

EUREKA
MATH

Name _____ Date _____

1.  Solve.

    a.  36,000 × 10 = _____

    b.  36,000 ÷ 10 = _____

    c.  4.3 × 10 = _____

    d.  4.3 ÷ 10 = _____

    e.  2.4 × 100 = _____

    f.  24 ÷ 1,000 = _____

    g.  4.54 × 1,000 = _____

    h.  3,045.4 ÷ 100 = _____

2.  Find the products.

    a.  14,560 × 10    = _____

    b.  14,560 × 100   = _____

    c.  14,560 × 1,000 = _____

    Explain how you decided on the number of zeros in the products for (a), (b), and (c).

EUREKA MATH

Lesson 2:   Reason abstractly using place value understanding to relate adjacent base ten units from millions to thousandths.

45

© 2015 Great Minds. eureka-math.org
G5-M1-TE-B1-1.3.1-1.2016

3. Find the quotients.

   a.  16.5 ÷ 10  = _____

   b.  16.5 ÷ 100 = _____

   c.  Explain how you decided where to place the decimal in the quotients for (a) and (b).

4. Ted says that 3 tenths multiplied by 100 equals 300 thousandths. Is he correct? Use a place value chart to explain your answer.

5. Alaska has a land area of about 1,700,000 square kilometers. Florida has a land area $\frac{1}{10}$ the size of Alaska. What is the land area of Florida? Explain how you found your answer.

Lesson 2:     Reason abstractly using place value understanding to relate adjacent base ten units from millions to thousandths.

© 2015 Great Minds. eureka-math.org
G5-M1-TE-B1-1.3.1-1.2016

EUREKA
MATH

# Lesson 3

Objective: Use exponents to name place value units, and explain patterns in the placement of the decimal point.

## Suggested Lesson Structure

■ Fluency Practice          (15 minutes)
■ Application Problem        (7 minutes)
■ Concept Development        (28 minutes)
■ Student Debrief           (10 minutes)

   **Total Time**              **(60 minutes)**

## Fluency Practice  (15 minutes)

- Sprint: Multiply by 3  **3.OA.7**                              (8 minutes)
- State the Unit as a Decimal—Choral Response  **5.NBT.2**       (4 minutes)
- Multiply and Divide by 10, 100, and 1000  **5.NBT.2**         (3 minutes)

### Sprint:  Multiply by 3  (8 minutes)

Materials:    (S) Multiply by 3 Sprint.

Note:  This Sprint reviews foundational skills learned in Grades 3 and 4.

### State the Unit as a Decimal—Choral Response  (4 minutes)

Note:  Reviewing these skills helps students work toward mastery of decimal place value, which assists them in applying their place value skills to more difficult concepts.

    T:    (Write 9 tenths = _____.) Complete the number sentence by saying the unknown value as a decimal.
    S:    0.9
    T:    (Write 10 tenths = _____.)
    S:    1.0
    T:    (Write 11 tenths = _____.)
    S:    1.1
    T:    (Write 12 tenths = _____.)
    S:    1.2

**EUREKA MATH**

Lesson 3:     Use exponents to name place value units, and explain patterns in the
placement of the decimal point.

© 2015 Great Minds. eureka-math.org
G5-M1-TE-B1-1.3.1-1.2016

47

T:    (Write 18 tenths = _____.)

S:    1.8

T:    (Write 28 tenths = _____.)

S:    2.8

T:    (Write 58 tenths = _____.)

S:    5.8

Repeat the process for 9 hundredths, 10 hundredths, 20 hundredths, 60 hundredths, 65 hundredths, 87 hundredths, and 118 tenths. (The last item is an extension.)

## Multiply and Divide by 10, 100, and 1000  (3 minutes)

Materials:    (S) Millions through thousandths place value chart (Lesson 1 Template)

Note:  This fluency drill reviews concepts taught in Lesson 2.

T:    (Project the place value chart from millions through thousandths.) Draw two disks in the thousandths place, and write the value below it.

S:    (Draw two disks in the thousandths column. Below it, write 0.002 in the appropriate place value columns.)

T:    Multiply by 10. Cross out each disk and the number 2 to show that you're changing its value.

S:    (Cross out each 1 thousandths disk and the 2. Draw arrows to the hundredths column, and draw two disks there. Below it, they write 2 in the hundredths column and 0 in the ones and tenths column.)

Repeat the process for the following possible sequence: 0.004 × 100, 0.004 × 1000, 1.004 × 1000, 1.024 × 100, 1.324 × 100, 1.324 × 10, and 1.324 × 1000.

Repeat the process for dividing by 10, 100, and 1000 for the following possible sequence: 4 ÷ 1, 4.1 ÷ 10, 4.1 ÷ 100, 41 ÷ 1000, and 123 ÷ 1000.

> **NOTES ON MULTIPLE MEANS OF ACTION AND EXPRESSION:**
>
> Very large numbers like one million and beyond easily capture the imagination of students. Consider allowing students to research and present to classmates the origin of number names like *googol* and *googleplex*. Connections to literacy can also be made with books about large numbers, such as *How Much is a Million* by Steven Kellogg, *A Million Dots* by Andrew Clements, or *Big Numbers and Pictures That Show Just How Big They Are* by Edward Packard and Sal Murdocca.
>
> The following benchmarks may help students appreciate just how large a googol is.
>
> - There are approximately $10^{24}$ stars in the observable universe.
> - There are approximately $10^{80}$ atoms in the observable universe.
> - A stack of 70 numbered cards can be ordered in approximately 1 googol different ways. That means that the number of ways a stack of only 70 cards can be shuffled is more than the number of atoms in the observable universe.

## Application Problem  (7 minutes)

Jack and Kevin are creating a mosaic for art class by using fragments of broken tiles. They want the mosaic to have 100 sections. If each section requires 31.5 tiles, how many tiles will they need to complete the mosaic? Explain your reasoning with a place value chart.

Note:  This Application Problem provides an opportunity for students to reason about the value of digits after being multiplied by 100.

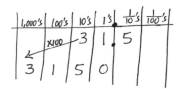

$31.5 \times 100 = 3{,}150$

They will need 3,150 tiles to complete the mosaic.

Lesson 3:    Use exponents to name place value units, and explain patterns in the placement of the decimal point.

© 2015 Great Minds. eureka-math.org
G5-M1-TE-B1-1.3.1-1.2016

**EUREKA MATH**

## Concept Development  (28 minutes)

Materials:    (S) Powers of 10 chart (Template), personal white board

**Problem 1**

T:    (Draw or project the powers of 10 chart, adding numerals as the discussion unfolds.)

|  |  |  |  | 100 | 10 |
|---|---|---|---|---|---|
|  |  |  |  | $10 \times 10$ | $10 \times 1$ |
|  |  |  |  |  |  |
|  |  |  |  |  |  |

T:    (Write $10 \times$ _____ $= 10$ on the board.) On your personal board, fill in the unknown factor to complete this number sentence.

S:    $10 \times 1 = 10$.

T:    (Write $10 \times$ _____ $= 100$ on the board.) Fill in the unknown factor to complete this number sentence.

S:    $10 \times 10 = 100$.

T:    This time, using only 10 as a factor, how could you multiply to get a product of 1,000? Write the multiplication sentence on your personal board.

S:    $10 \times 10 \times 10 = 1{,}000$.

**MP.7**

T:    Work with your partner. What would the multiplication sentence be for 10,000 using only 10 as a factor? Write it on your personal board.

S:    (Write.)

T:    How many factors of 10 did we have to multiply to get to 1,000?

S:    3.

T:    How many factors of 10 do we have to multiply to get 10,000?

S:    4.

T:    Say the number sentence.

S:    $10 \times 10 \times 10 \times 10 = 10{,}000$.

T:    How many zeros are in our product of 10,000?

S:    4 zeros.

T:    What patterns do you notice? Turn and share with your partner.

S:    The number of zeros is the same on both sides of the equation. → The number of zeros in the product is the same as the total number of zeros in the factors. → I see three zeros on the left side, and there are three zeros on the right side for $10 \times 10 \times 10 = 1{,}000$. → The 1 moves one place to the left every time we multiply by 10. → It's like a place value chart. Each number is 10 times as much as the last one.

Lesson 3:       Use exponents to name place value units, and explain patterns in the              49
                placement of the decimal point.

© 2015 Great Minds. eureka-math.org
G5-M1-TE-B1-1.3.1-1.2016

MP.7

T:   Using this pattern, how many factors of 10 do we have to multiply to get 1 million? Work with your partner to write the multiplication sentence.

S:   (Write.)

T:   How many factors of 10 did you use?

S:   6.

T:   Why did we need 6 factors of 10?

S:   1 million has 6 zeros.

T:   (Write the term *exponent* on the board.) We can use an **exponent** to represent how many times we use 10 as a factor. We can write $10 \times 10$ as $10^2$. (Add to the chart.) We say, "Ten to the second power." The 2 (point to exponent) is the exponent, and it tells us how many times to use 10 as a factor.

T:   How do you express 1000 using exponents? Turn and share with your partner.

S:   We multiply $10 \times 10 \times 10$, which is three times, so the answer is $10^3$. → There are three zeros in 1,000, so it's ten to the third power.

T:   Working with your partner, complete the chart using the exponents to represent each value on the place value chart.

| 1,000,000 | 100,000 | 10,000 | 1,000 | 100 | 10 |
|---|---|---|---|---|---|
| $(10 \times 10 \times 10) \times (10 \times 10 \times 10)$ | $10 \times 10 \times (10 \times 10 \times 10)$ | $10 \times (10 \times 10 \times 10)$ | $(10 \times 10 \times 10)$ | $10 \times 10$ | $10 \times 1$ |
| $10^6$ | $10^5$ | $10^4$ | $10^3$ | $10^2$ | $10^1$ |

After reviewing the chart with the students, challenge them to multiply 10 one hundred times. As some start to write it out, others may write $10^{100}$, a googol, with exponents.

T:   Now, look at the place value chart. Let's read our powers of 10 and the equivalent values.

S:   Ten to the second power equals 100. Ten to the third power equals 1,000. (Continue to read chorally up to 1 million.)

T:   A googol has 100 zeros. Write it using an exponent on your personal board.

S:   (Write $10^{100}$.)

**Problem 2**

$10^5$

T:   Write *ten to the fifth power* as a product of tens.

S:   $10^5 = 10 \times 10 \times 10 \times 10 \times 10$.

T:   Find the product.

S:   $10^5 = 100,000$.

Repeat with more examples as needed.

NOTES ON
MULTIPLE MEANS
OF REPRESENTATION:

Providing non-examples is a powerful way to clear up mathematical misconceptions and generate conversation around the work. Highlight those examples such as $10^5$ pointing out its equality to $10 \times 10 \times 10 \times 10 \times 10$ but not to $10 \times 5$ or even $5^{10}$.

Allowing students to explore with a calculator and highlighting the functions used to calculate these expressions (e.g., $10^5$ versus $10 \times 5$) can be valuable.

© 2015 Great Minds. eureka-math.org
G5-M1-TE-B1-1.3.1-1.2016

**Problem 3**

$10 \times 100$

T: Work with your partner to write this expression using an exponent on your personal board. Explain your reasoning.

S: I multiply $10 \times 100$ to get 1,000, so the answer is ten to the third power. → There are 3 factors of 10. → There are three tens. I can see one 10 in the first factor and two more tens in the second factor.

Repeat with $100 \times 1000$ and other examples as needed.

**Problem 4**

$3 \times 10^2$

$3.4 \times 10^3$

T: Compare these expressions to the ones we've already talked about.

S: These have factors other than 10.

T: Write $3 \times 10^2$ without using an exponent. Write it on your personal board.

S: $3 \times 100$.

T: What's the product?

S: 300.

T: If you know that $3 \times 100$ equals 300, then what is $3 \times 10^2$? Turn and explain to your partner.

S: The product is also 300. $10^2$ and 100 are the same amount, so the product will be the same.

T: Use what you learned about multiplying decimals by 10, 100, and 1,000 and your new knowledge about exponents to solve $3.4 \times 10^3$ with your partner.

S: $3.4 \times 10^3 = 3,400$.

Repeat with $4.021 \times 10^2$ and other examples as needed.

Have students share their solutions and reasoning about multiplying decimal factors by powers of 10. In particular, students should articulate the relationship between the exponent, how the values of the digits change, and the placement of the decimal in the product.

**Problem 5**

$700 \div 10^2$

$7.1 \div 10^2$

T: Write $700 \div 10^2$ without using an exponent, and find the quotient. Write it on your personal board.

S: $700 \div 100 = 7$.

T: If you know that $700 \div 100$ equals 7, then what is $700 \div 10^2$? Turn and explain to your partner.

S: The quotient is 7 because $10^2 = 100$. → 7 hundreds divided by 1 hundred equals 7.

T: Use what you know about dividing decimals by multiples of 10 and your new knowledge about exponents to solve $7.1 \div 10^2$ with your partner.

S: (Work.)

T: Tell your partner what you notice about the relationship between the exponents and how the values of the digits change. Discuss how you decided where to place the decimal.

Repeat with more examples as needed.

Lesson 3: Use exponents to name place value units, and explain patterns in the placement of the decimal point.

© 2015 Great Minds. eureka-math.org
G5-M1-TE-B1-1.3.1-1.2016

**Problem 6**

Complete this pattern:  0.043     4.3     430     _____     _____     _____

    T:  (Write the pattern on the board.) Turn and talk with your partner about the pattern on the board. How is the value of the 4 changing as we move to the next term in the sequence? Draw a place value chart to explain your ideas as you complete the pattern, and use an exponent to express the relationships.

    S:  The 4 shifted two places to the left. → Each number is being multiplied by 100 to get the next one. → Each number is multiplied by 10 twice. → Each number is multiplied by $10^2$.

Repeat with 6,300,000; ____; 630; 6.3; _____ and other patterns as needed.

    T:  As you work on the Problem Set, be sure you are thinking about the patterns that we've discovered today.

## Problem Set  (10 minutes)

Students should do their personal best to complete the Problem Set within the allotted 10 minutes. For some classes, it may be appropriate to modify the assignment by specifying which problems they work on first. Some problems do not specify a method for solving. Students solve these problems using the RDW approach used for Application Problems.

## Student Debrief  (10 minutes)

**Lesson Objective:**  Use exponents to name place value units, and explain patterns in the placement of the decimal point.

The Student Debrief is intended to invite reflection and active processing of the total lesson experience.

Invite students to review their solutions for the Problem Set. They should check work by comparing answers with a partner before going over answers as a class. Look for misconceptions or misunderstandings that can be addressed in the Debrief. Guide students in a conversation to debrief the Problem Set and process the lesson.

Any combination of the questions below may be used to lead the discussion.

- What is an **exponent,** and how can exponents be useful in representing numbers? (This question could also serve as a prompt for math journals. Journaling about new vocabulary throughout the year can be a powerful way for students to solidify their understanding of new terms.)

The student work sample shows:

Name: Yi Ting

1. Write the following in exponential form (e.g., 100 = $10^2$).
   - a. 10,000 = $10^4$
   - b. 1,000 = $10^3$
   - c. 10 × 10 = $10^2$
   - d. 100 × 100 = $10^4$
   - e. 1,000,000 = $10^6$
   - f. 1,000 × 1,000 = $10^6$

2. Write the following in standard form (e.g., 5 × $10^2$ = 500).
   - a. 9 × $10^3$ = 9,000
   - b. 39 × $10^4$ = 390,000
   - c. 7,200 ÷ $10^2$ = 72
   - d. 7,200,000 ÷ $10^3$ = 7,200
   - e. 4.025 × $10^3$ = 4,025
   - f. 40.25 × $10^4$ = 402,500
   - g. 72.5 ÷ $10^2$ = 0.725
   - h. 7.2 ÷ $10^2$ = 0.072

3. Think about the answers to Problem 2(a–d). Explain the pattern used to find an answer when you multiply or divide a whole number by a power of 10.

   The exponent tells you how many places to shift the digits. If multiplying, the digits shift to the left. If dividing, the digits shift to the right.

4. Think about the answers to Problem 2(e–h). Explain the pattern used to place the decimal in the answer when you multiply or divide a decimal by a power of 10.

   When you multiply a decimal by a power of 10, the exponent will tell you how many places the digits will shift to the left of the decimal. When you divide, the digits will shift to the right of the decimal depending on the power of 10.

© 2015 Great Minds. eureka-math.org
G5-M1-TE-B1-1.3.1-1.2016

- How would you write 1,000 using exponents? How would you write it as a multiplication sentence using only 10 as a factor?

- Explain to your partner the relationship we saw between the exponents and the number of places the digits shift when you multiplied or divided by a power of 10.

- How are the patterns you discovered in Problems 3 and 4 of the Problem Set alike?

- Give students plenty of opportunity to discuss the error patterns in Problems 6(a) and 6(b). These are the most common misconceptions students hold when dealing with exponents, so it is worth the time to see that they do not become firmly held.

## Exit Ticket  (3 minutes)

After the Student Debrief, instruct students to complete the Exit Ticket. A review of their work will help with assessing students' understanding of the concepts that were presented in today's lesson and planning more effectively for future lessons. The questions may be read aloud to the students.

5.  Complete the patterns.

a.  0.03   0.3   __3__   30   __300__   __3,000__

b.  6,500,000   65,000   __650__   6.5   __0.065__

c.  __94,300__   9,430   __943__   94.3   9.43   __0.943__

d.  999   9990   99,900   __999,000__   __9,990,000__   99,900,000

e.  __0.075__   7.5   750   75,000   __7,500,000__   750,000,000

f.  Explain how you found the unknown numbers in set (b). Be sure to include your reasoning about the number of zeros in your numbers and how you placed the decimal.

I saw the second number in the pattern had 2 zeros less than the first. The pattern is to divide by $10^2$. The digits must shift 2 places to the right.

g.  Explain how you found the unknown numbers in set (d). Be sure to include your reasoning about the number of zeros in your numbers and how you placed the decimal.

I saw the second number in the pattern had 1 more zero than the first. The pattern is to multiply by 10. The digits must shift 1 place to the left.

6.  Shaunnie and Marlon missed the lesson on exponents. Shaunnie incorrectly wrote $10^5 = 50$ on her paper, and Marlon incorrectly wrote $2.5 \times 10^2 = 2,500$ on his paper.

a.  What mistake has Shaunnie made? Explain using words, numbers, or pictures why her thinking is incorrect and what she needs to do to correct her answer.

Shaunnie is thinking $10^5$ means 10×5 which is 50. $10^5$ means 10×10×10×10×10 which is 100,000.

b.  What mistake has Marlon made? Explain using words, numbers, or pictures why his thinking is incorrect and what he needs to do to correct his answer.

Marlon multiplied 2.5 by $10^3$ instead of $10^2$. Perhaps he added zeros to the end of the number rather than shifting digits in a place value chart.

Lesson 3:   Use exponents to name place value units, and explain patterns in the placement of the decimal point.

53

© 2015 Great Minds. eureka-math.org
G5-M1-TE-B1-1.3.1-1.2016

# A

Number Correct: _____

Multiply by 3

| | | |
|---|---|---|
| 1. | 1 × 3 = | |
| 2. | 3 × 1 = | |
| 3. | 2 × 3 = | |
| 4. | 3 × 2 = | |
| 5. | 3 × 3 = | |
| 6. | 4 × 3 = | |
| 7. | 3 × 4 = | |
| 8. | 5 × 3 = | |
| 9. | 3 × 5 = | |
| 10. | 6 × 3 = | |
| 11. | 3 × 6 = | |
| 12. | 7 × 3 = | |
| 13. | 3 × 7 = | |
| 14. | 8 × 3 = | |
| 15. | 3 × 8 = | |
| 16. | 9 × 3 = | |
| 17. | 3 × 9 = | |
| 18. | 10 × 3 = | |
| 19. | 3 × 10 = | |
| 20. | 3 × 3 = | |
| 21. | 1 × 3 = | |
| 22. | 2 × 3 = | |

| | | |
|---|---|---|
| 23. | 10 × 3 = | |
| 24. | 9 × 3 = | |
| 25. | 4 × 3 = | |
| 26. | 8 × 3 = | |
| 27. | 5 × 3 = | |
| 28. | 7 × 3 = | |
| 29. | 6 × 3 = | |
| 30. | 3 × 10 = | |
| 31. | 3 × 5 = | |
| 32. | 3 × 6 = | |
| 33. | 3 × 1 = | |
| 34. | 3 × 9 = | |
| 35. | 3 × 4 = | |
| 36. | 3 × 3 = | |
| 37. | 3 × 2 = | |
| 38. | 3 × 7 = | |
| 39. | 3 × 8 = | |
| 40. | 11 × 3 = | |
| 41. | 3 × 11 = | |
| 42. | 12 × 3 = | |
| 43. | 3 × 13 = | |
| 44. | 13 × 3 = | |

Lesson 3: Use exponents to name place value units, and explain patterns in the placement of the decimal point.

EUREKA MATH

# B

Number Correct: _____

Improvement: _____

Multiply by 3

| | | | | | | |
|---|---|---|---|---|---|---|
| 1. | $3 \times 1 =$ | | 23. | $9 \times 3 =$ | |
| 2. | $1 \times 3 =$ | | 24. | $3 \times 3 =$ | |
| 3. | $3 \times 2 =$ | | 25. | $8 \times 3 =$ | |
| 4. | $2 \times 3 =$ | | 26. | $4 \times 3 =$ | |
| 5. | $3 \times 3 =$ | | 27. | $7 \times 3 =$ | |
| 6. | $3 \times 4 =$ | | 28. | $5 \times 3 =$ | |
| 7. | $4 \times 3 =$ | | 29. | $6 \times 3 =$ | |
| 8. | $3 \times 5 =$ | | 30. | $3 \times 5 =$ | |
| 9. | $5 \times 3 =$ | | 31. | $3 \times 10 =$ | |
| 10. | $3 \times 6 =$ | | 32. | $3 \times 1 =$ | |
| 11. | $6 \times 3 =$ | | 33. | $3 \times 6 =$ | |
| 12. | $3 \times 7 =$ | | 34. | $3 \times 4 =$ | |
| 13. | $7 \times 3 =$ | | 35. | $3 \times 9 =$ | |
| 14. | $3 \times 8 =$ | | 36. | $3 \times 2 =$ | |
| 15. | $8 \times 3 =$ | | 37. | $3 \times 7 =$ | |
| 16. | $3 \times 9 =$ | | 38. | $3 \times 3 =$ | |
| 17. | $9 \times 3 =$ | | 39. | $3 \times 8 =$ | |
| 18. | $3 \times 10 =$ | | 40. | $11 \times 3 =$ | |
| 19. | $10 \times 3 =$ | | 41. | $3 \times 11 =$ | |
| 20. | $1 \times 3 =$ | | 42. | $13 \times 3 =$ | |
| 21. | $10 \times 3 =$ | | 43. | $3 \times 13 =$ | |
| 22. | $2 \times 3 =$ | | 44. | $12 \times 3 =$ | |

**EUREKA MATH**®

**Lesson 3:**   Use exponents to name place value units, and explain patterns in the placement of the decimal point.

55

Name _____ Date _____

1.  Write the following in exponential form (e.g., $100 = 10^2$).

    a.  $10,000 =$ _____

    b.  $1,000 =$ _____

    c.  $10 \times 10 =$ _____

    d.  $100 \times 100 =$ _____

    e.  $1,000,000 =$ _____

    f.  $1,000 \times 1,000 =$ _____

2.  Write the following in standard form (e.g., $5 \times 10^2 = 500$).

    a.  $9 \times 10^3 =$ _____

    b.  $39 \times 10^4 =$ _____

    c.  $7,200 \div 10^2 =$ _____

    d.  $7,200,000 \div 10^3 =$ _____

    e.  $4.025 \times 10^3 =$ _____

    f.  $40.25 \times 10^4 =$ _____

    g.  $72.5 \div 10^2 =$ _____

    h.  $7.2 \div 10^2 =$ _____

3.  Think about the answers to Problem 2(a–d). Explain the pattern used to find an answer when you multiply or divide a whole number by a power of 10.

4.  Think about the answers to Problem 2(e–h). Explain the pattern used to place the decimal in the answer when you multiply or divide a decimal by a power of 10.

Lesson 3:   Use exponents to name place value units, and explain patterns in the placement of the decimal point.

EUREKA
MATH

5. Complete the patterns.

   a.  0.03  0.3  _____  30  _____  _____

   b.  6,500,000  65,000  _____  6.5  _____

   c.  _____  9,430  _____  94.3  9.43  _____

   d.  999  9990  99,900  _____  _____  _____

   e.  _____  7.5  750  75,000  _____  _____

   f.  Explain how you found the unknown numbers in set (b). Be sure to include your reasoning about the number of zeros in your numbers and how you placed the decimal.

   g.  Explain how you found the unknown numbers in set (d). Be sure to include your reasoning about the number of zeros in your numbers and how you placed the decimal.

6. Shaunnie and Marlon missed the lesson on exponents. Shaunnie incorrectly wrote $10^5 = 50$ on her paper, and Marlon incorrectly wrote $2.5 \times 10^2 = 2.500$ on his paper.

   a.  What mistake has Shaunnie made? Explain using words, numbers, or pictures why her thinking is incorrect and what she needs to do to correct her answer.

   b.  What mistake has Marlon made? Explain using words, numbers, or pictures why his thinking is incorrect and what he needs to do to correct his answer.

Lesson 3:    Use exponents to name place value units, and explain patterns in the placement of the decimal point.

© 2015 Great Minds. eureka-math.org
G5-M1-TE-B1-1.3.1-1.2016

Name _____     Date _____

1.  Write the following in exponential form and as a multiplication sentence using only 10 as a factor (e.g., $100 = 10^2 = 10 \times 10$).

    a.  1,000         = _____ = _____

    b.  $100 \times 100$    = _____ = _____

2.  Write the following in standard form (e.g., $4 \times 10^2 = 400$).

    a.  $3 \times 10^2 =$ _____

    c.  $800 \div 10^3 =$ _____

    b.  $2.16 \times 10^4 =$ _____

    d.  $754.2 \div 10^2 =$ _____

**Lesson 3:**     Use exponents to name place value units, and explain patterns in the placement of the decimal point.

EUREKA
MATH

Name _____     Date _____

1.  Write the following in exponential form (e.g., 100 = $10^2$).

    a.  1000 = _____        d.  100 × 10 = _____

    b.  10 × 10 = _____     e.  1,000,000 = _____

    c.  100,000 = _____     f.  10,000 × 10 = _____

2.  Write the following in standard form (e.g., 4 × $10^2$ = 400).

    a.  4 × $10^3$ = _____        e.  6.072 × $10^3$ = _____

    b.  64 × $10^4$ = _____       f.  60.72 × $10^4$ = _____

    c.  5,300 ÷ $10^2$ = _____    g.  948 ÷ $10^3$ = _____

    d.  5,300,000 ÷ $10^3$ = _____    h.  9.4 ÷ $10^2$ = _____

3.  Complete the patterns.

    a.  0.02    0.2    _____    20    _____    _____

    b.  3,400,000    34,000    _____    3.4    _____

    c.  _____    8,570    _____    85.7    8.57    _____

    d.  444    4440    44,400    _____    _____    _____

    e.  _____    9.5    950    95,000    _____    _____

EUREKA
MATH®

Lesson 3:       Use exponents to name place value units, and explain patterns in the        59
                placement of the decimal point.

© 2015 Great Minds. eureka-math.org
G5-M1-TE-B1-1.3.1-1.2016

4. After a lesson on exponents, Tia went home and said to her mom, "I learned that $10^4$ is the same as 40,000." She has made a mistake in her thinking. Use words, numbers, or a place value chart to help Tia correct her mistake.

5. Solve $247 \div 10^2$ and $247 \times 10^2$.

   a. What is different about the two answers? Use words, numbers, or pictures to explain how the digits shift.

   b. Based on the answers from the pair of expressions above, solve $247 \div 10^3$ and $247 \times 10^3$.

Lesson 3:    Use exponents to name place value units, and explain patterns in the placement of the decimal point.

EUREKA MATH

| 10 | | |
|---|---|---|
| $10 \times$ ___ | | |
| | | |
| | | |
| | | |
| | | |

powers of 10 chart

Lesson 3:   Use exponents to name place value units, and explain patterns in the placement of the decimal point.

61

# Lesson 4

Objective:  Use exponents to denote powers of 10 with application to metric conversions.

## Suggested Lesson Structure

■ Fluency Practice          (12 minutes)
■ Application Problem        (8 minutes)
■ Concept Development        (30 minutes)
■ Student Debrief           (10 minutes)

**Total Time**              **(60 minutes)**

## Fluency Practice  (12 minutes)

- Multiply and Divide Decimals by 10, 100, and 1000  **5.NBT.2**          (5 minutes)
- Write the Unit as a Decimal  **5.NBT.1**          (2 minutes)
- Write in Exponential Form  **5.NBT.2**          (3 minutes)
- Convert Units  **4.MD.1**          (2 minutes)

### Multiply and Divide Decimals by 10, 100, and 1000  (5 minutes)

Materials:    (S) Millions through thousandths place value chart (Lesson 1 template), personal white board

Note:  This fluency activity reviews concepts taught in earlier lessons and helps students work toward mastery in multiplying and dividing decimals by 10, 100, and 1000.

  T:    (Project the place value chart from millions to thousandths. Draw 3 disks in the tens place, 2 disks in the ones place, and 4 disks in the tenths place.) Say the value as a decimal.

  S:    32.4 (thirty-two and four tenths).

  T:    Write the number on your personal boards, and multiply it by 10.

  S:    (Write 32.4 on their place value charts, cross out each digit, and shift the number one place value to the left to show 324.)

  T:    Show 32.4 divided by 10.

  S:    (Write 32.4 on their place value charts, cross out each digit, and shift the number one place value to the right to show 3.24.)

Repeat the process and sequence for 32.4 × 100, 32.4 ÷ 100, 837 ÷ 1000, and 0.418 × 1000.

EUREKA
MATH

## Write the Unit as a Decimal  (2 minutes)

Materials:    (S) Personal white board

Note:  Reviewing these skills helps students work toward mastery of decimal place value. This, in turn, helps them apply their place value skills to more difficult concepts.

    T:    (Write 9 tenths on the board.) Show this unit form as a decimal.

    S:    0.9.

    T:    (Write 10 tenths on the board.)

    S:    1.0.

Repeat the process for 20 tenths, 30 tenths, 70 tenths, 9 hundredths, 10 hundredths, 11 hundredths, 17 hundredths, 57 hundredths, 42 hundredths, 9 thousandths, 10 thousandths, 20 thousandths, 60 thousandths, 64 thousandths, and 83 thousandths.

## Write in Exponential Form  (3 minutes)

Materials:    (S) Personal white board

Note:  Reviewing this skill in isolation lays a foundation for students to apply it when multiplying during the lesson.

    T:    (Write $100 = 10^?$.) Write 100 in exponential form.

    S:    (Write $100 = 10^2$.)

Repeat the process for 1,000, 10,000, and 1,000,000.

## Convert Units  (2 minutes)

Materials:    (S) Personal white board

Note:  Reviewing conversions in isolation lays a foundation for students to apply it when multiplying and dividing during the lesson.

Use this quick fluency drill to activate prior knowledge of these familiar equivalents.

    T:    (Write 1 km = _____ m.) Fill in the unknown number.

    S:    (Write 1 km = 1,000 m.)

Repeat the process and procedure for 1 kg = _____ g, 1 liter = _____ mL, 1 m = _____ cm.

**EUREKA MATH**®

Lesson 4:    Use exponents to denote powers of 10 with application to metric conversions.

## Application Problem  (8 minutes)

Materials:  (S) Meter strip (Template)

T:  Here is a place value chart. (Show the place value chart from thousands to thousandths without other headings.)

| thousands | hundreds | tens | ones | tenths | hundredths | thousandths |
|---|---|---|---|---|---|---|
| 1000 meters<br>kilometer | 100 meters<br>(hectometer) | 10 meters<br>(dekameter) | 1 meter | $\frac{1}{10}$ meter<br>(decimeter) | $\frac{1}{100}$ meter<br>centimeter | $\frac{1}{1,000}$ meter<br>**millimeter** |
|  |  |  | 0 | 0 | 1 |  |
|  |  |  | 0 | 0 | 0 | 1 |

T:  Here is a set of column headings based on metric length related to our place value chart, designating one meter as the base unit, or the ones place.

T:  Use your meter strip to show and explain to your partner the lengths that relate to the tenths, hundredths, and thousandths places. (Move through the tenths, hundredths, and thousandths until identifying and naming $\frac{1}{1,000}$ meter as 1 **millimeter**.)

Have students then explain to their partner lengths that relate to the tens, hundreds, and thousands places. For example, 10 meters would be about the length of the classroom, 100 meters about the length of a football field, and 1,000 meters is a kilometer, which may be conceived in relation to the distance to their home from school.

Note:  Be sure to establish the following, which is essential to the Concept Development lesson:

1 **millimeter** (mm) = $\frac{1}{1000}$ meter (m) = 0.001 meter

1 centimeter (cm) = $\frac{1}{100}$ meter (m) = 0.01 meter.

The relationship of metric lengths to the place value chart will also help students to realize when they are moving from smaller to larger or larger to smaller units. Consider reviewing the multiplicative relationships between the units.

**NOTES ON MULTIPLE MEANS OF ACTION AND ENGAGEMENT:**

The place value chart can be used throughout the coming lesson to help students think through whether they are renaming from small to large units or large to small units. Throughout the school day, take the opportunity to extend thinking by asking students to make a conversion to the unit that is 1 tenth as large as a meter (decimeter) and the unit 10 times as large (dekameter). Students can do research about these and other metric units that are less commonly used or investigate industry applications for the less familiar units. For example, decameters are often used to measure altitude in meteorology, and decimeters are commonly used in physical chemistry.

Lesson 4:  Use exponents to denote powers of 10 with application to metric conversions.

EUREKA MATH

## Concept Development  (30 minutes)

Materials:    (S) Meter strip (Template), personal white board

Each problem below includes conversions from both large units to smaller units and small to larger units. Allow students the time to reason about how the change in the size of the unit will affect the *quantity* and *size* of the units needed to express an equivalent measure.

**Problem 1**

Rename or convert large units as smaller units using multiplication equations with exponents.

T:    (Draw and label a line 2 meters long on the board.)

T:    How many centimeters equal 2 meters?

S:    200 centimeters. (Label the same 2 meter point as 200 centimeters. Fill in the first row of the t-chart.)

T:    Tell me a multiplication equation multiplying by 2 to get 200.

S:    $2 \times 100 = 200$.

T:    Restate the equation renaming 100 with an exponent.

S:    $2 \times 10^2 = 200$.

T:    With your partner, determine how many centimeters are equal to 1.37 meter. Use your meter strip if it helps you.

S:    It's 1 meter and 37 centimeters. → It's more than 1 meter and less than 2 meters. → 37 hundredths of a meter is 37 centimeters. 100 cm + 37 cm = 137 cm.

T:    What is the equivalent measure in centimeters?

S:    137 centimeters. (On the board, label the same 1.37 meter point as 137 centimeters. Fill in the second row of the chart.)

T:    On your boards, show this conversion using a multiplication equation with an exponent.

S:    $1.37 \times 100 = 137$. → $1.37 \times 10^2 = 137$.

T:    What must we do to the number of meters to rename them as centimeters?

S:    Multiply the number of meters by 100 or $10^2$. (Record the rule on the chart. Repeat with 2.6 meters.)

T:    How can we use multiplication to rename a meter as millimeters? Discuss with your partner.

S:    Multiply the number of meters by 1,000 or by $10^3$.

NOTES ON MULTIPLE MEANS OF REPRESENTATION:

The drawing of the 2-meter, 200-centimeter, and 2,000-millimeter line supports student understanding, especially when plotting 1.37 meters. Butcher paper can be used if there is insufficient space on the class board or other surface normally used. This also promotes student success with plotting decimal fractions on the number line.

| meters | centimeters | millimeters |
|---|---|---|
| 2 | 200 | 2,000 |
| 1.37 | 137 | 1,370 |
| 2.6 | 260 | 2,600 |

To rename meters as centimeters, multiply by $10^2$.
To rename meters as millimeters, multiply by $10^3$.

Lesson 4:    Use exponents to denote powers of 10 with application to metric conversions.

65

© 2015 Great Minds. eureka-math.org
G5-M1-TE-B1-1.3.1-1.2016

T:   Take a moment to write multiplication equations with exponents to find the number of millimeters to complete the third column of our chart.

T:   Show me your boards.

S:   (Show $2 \times 10^3 = 2,000$, $1.37 \times 10^3 = 1,370$, and $2.6 \times 10^3 = 2,600$.)

T/S: (Fill in the equivalent millimeter measures together.)

T:   Explain the difference between A and B to your partner.

| *Problem A* | *Problem B* |
|---|---|
| 2 meters $\times 10^3$ = 2,000 meters | $2 \times 10^3 = 2,000$   2 meters = 2,000 millimeters |

S:   Problem A is not renaming or converting, but multiplying 2 *meters* by $10^3$, so the answer is 2,000 *meters.* That's more than 2 miles! → Problem B is renaming by multiplying 1,000 by 2 because each meter has a thousand millimeters in it. After we multiply, then we can name the unit. That is the exact same measurement as 2 meters.

T:   Yes, we are multiplying the number of meters by $10^3$. Explain why we multiply to rename large units as small units. (Point to the 2-meter line drawn on the board.)

S:   1 meter = 1,000 millimeters, 2 meters = 2,000 millimeters. It's the *number* of meters that is being multiplied, not the meters. → Multiplying didn't make 2 meters into more *meters,* but renamed the 2 meters as 2,000 millimeters. → One meter got chopped up into 1,000 millimeters, so we multiply the number of meters by 1,000. → The length stays the same because we're making more units by decomposing a meter, not by making more copies of a meter.

## Problem 2

Rename millimeters and centimeters as meters using division equations with exponents.

Again, using the 2-meter line and chart, reverse Problem 1's sequence, and convert from smaller to larger units, dividing by $10^2$ to rename, or convert, centimeters as meters, dividing by $10^3$ to rename, or convert, millimeters as meters.

| millimeters | centimeters | meters |
|---|---|---|
| 2,000 | 200 | 2 |
| 1,370 | 137 | 1.37 |
| 2,600 | 260 | 2.6 |

To rename centimeters to meters, divide by $10^2$.
To rename millimeters to meters, divide by $10^3$.

Culminate with the same reflection:

T:   We are dividing the number of meters by $10^2$ or by $10^3$. That is a method for renaming centimeters as meters and millimeters as meters. Explain the difference between C and D with your partner.

| *Problem C* | *Problem D* |
|---|---|
| 2,000 mm $\div 10^3$ = 2 mm | $2,000 \div 10^3 = 2$   2,000 mm = 2 m |

S:   1,000 millimeters = 1 meter, 2,000 millimeters = 2 meters. It's the *number* of millimeters that is being divided, not the millimeters. → Division renamed the 2,000 mm as 2 meters. How many groups of 1,000 are in 2 thousands? → 1,000 millimeters got grouped together as 1 meter, so we divide or make groups of 1,000.

Lesson 4:      Use exponents to denote powers of 10 with application to metric conversions.

© 2015 Great Minds. eureka-math.org
G5-M1-TE-B1-1.3.1-1.2016

## Problem 3

A ribbon measures 4.5 meters. Convert its length to centimeters.
A wire measures 67 millimeters. Convert its length to meters.

Note: The most important concept is the equivalence of the two measurements—that is, the length did not change, which becomes very apparent when conversions are contextualized. The ribbon and wire are not getting longer or shorter. Clarify this understanding before moving on to finding the conversion equation by asking, "How can 4.5 and 4,500 represent the same length?" (While the numeric values differ, the unit size is also different. 4.5 is meters. 4,500 is millimeters. Meters are 1,000 times as large as millimeters. Therefore, it takes fewer meters to represent the same amount as something measured in millimeters.) Lead students to articulate that when converting the number of large units to a number of smaller units, they multiplied, and when converting from small units to larger units, they divided.

## Problem Set  (10 minutes)

Students should do their personal best to complete the Problem Set within the allotted 10 minutes. For some classes, it may be appropriate to modify the assignment by specifying which problems they work on first. Some problems do not specify a method for solving. Students solve these problems using the RDW approach used for Application Problems.

In this Problem Set, we suggest all students begin with Problem 1 and leave Problem 6 for the end, if they have time.

## Student Debrief  (10 minutes)

**Lesson Objective:** Use exponents to denote powers of 10 with application to metric conversions.

The Student Debrief is intended to invite reflection and active processing of the total lesson experience.

---

Name __Janice_____  Date _____

1. Convert and write an equation with an exponent. Use your meter strip when it helps you.

   a. 3 meters to centimeters      3 m = 300 cm            $3 \times 10^2 = 300$
   b. 105 centimeters to meters    105 cm = __1.05__ m     $105 \div 10^2 = 1.05$
   c. 1.68 meters to centimeters   __1.68__ m = __168__ cm  $1.68 \times 10^2 = 168$
   d. 80 centimeters to meters     __80__ cm = __0.8__ m    $80 \div 10^2 = 0.8$
   e. 9.2 meters to centimeters    __9.2__ m = __920__ cm   $9.2 \times 10^2 = 920$
   f. 4 centimeters to meters      __4__ cm = __0.04__ m    $4 \div 10^2 = 0.04$

   g. In the space below, list the letters of the problems where larger units are converted to smaller units.

   a, c, and e.

2. Convert using an equation with an exponent. Use your meter strip when it helps you.

   a. 3 meters to millimeters        __3__ m = __3,000__ mm      $3 \times 10^3 = 3000$
   b. 1.2 meters to millimeters      __1.2__ m = __1,200__ mm    $1.2 \times 10^3 = 1,200$
   c. 1,020 millimeters to meters    __1,020__ mm = __1.02__ m   $1,020 \div 10^3 = 1.02$
   d. 97 millimeters to meters       __97__ mm = __0.097__ m     $97 \div 10^3 = 0.097$
   e. 7.28 meters to millimeters     __7.28__ m = __7,280__ mm   $7.28 \times 10^3 = 7,280$
   f. 4 millimeters to meters        __4__ mm = __0.004__ m      $4 \div 10^3 = 0.004$

   g. In the space below, list the letters of the problems where smaller units are converted to larger units.

   c, d, and f.

---

3. Read each aloud as you write the equivalent measures. Write an equation with an exponent you might use to convert.

   a. 3.512 m = __3,512__ mm        $3.512 \times 10^3 = 3,512$
   b. 8 cm = __0.08__ m             $8 \div 10^2 = 0.08$
   c. 42 mm = __0.042__ m           $42 \div 10^3 = 0.042$
   d. 0.05 m = __50__ mm            $0.05 \times 10^3 = 50$
   e. 0.002 m = __0.2__ cm          $0.002 \times 10^2 = 0.2$

4. The length of the bar for a high jump competition must always be 4.75 m. Express this measurement in millimeters. Explain your thinking including an equation with an exponent.

   4.75m = 4,750 mm
   Since 1m is equal to 1,000 mm, I multiplied $4.75 \times 10^3 = 4,750$.

5. A honey bee's length measures 1 cm. Express this measurement in meters. Explain your thinking including an equation with an exponent.

   1 cm = 0.01 m
   Since 1 m is equal to 100 cm, I divided $1 \div 10^2 = 0.01$.

6. Explain why converting from meters to centimeters uses a different exponent than converting from meters to millimeters.

   1 m can be unbundled into 100 cm. Each cm can be unbundled into 10 mm, so 1 m is the same as 1,000 mm.
   $1 m = 10^2 cm$.
   $1 m = 10^3 mm$.

---

Lesson 4:   Use exponents to denote powers of 10 with application to metric conversions.

67

© 2015 Great Minds. eureka-math.org
G5-M1-TE-B1-1.3.1-1.2016

Invite students to review their solutions for the Problem Set. They should check work by comparing answers with a partner before going over answers as a class. Look for misconceptions or misunderstandings that can be addressed in the Debrief. Guide students in a conversation to debrief the worksheet and process the lesson.

Any combination of the questions below may be used to lead the discussion.

- Which of the following statements is false? Explain your thinking to your partner.
    a. $2 \text{ m} \times 10^3 = 2{,}000 \text{ m}$
    b. $2 \text{ m} \times 10^3 = 2{,}000 \text{ mm}$
    c. $2 \times 10^3 = 2{,}000$
    d. $2 \text{ m} = 2{,}000 \text{ mm}$

- Is it easier for you to think about converting from large units to smaller units or small units to larger units? Why? What is the difference in both the thinking and the operation required?

- Let's look at the place value chart. Explain to your partner the way the equivalence of 2 meters, 20 tenth meters, 200 centimeters, and 2,000 **millimeters** is shown.

- How can we use what we know about renaming meters to millimeters to rename kilograms to grams and liters to milliliters?

| thousands $(1 \times 10^3)$ | hundreds $(1 \times 10^2)$ | tens $(1 \times 10^1)$ | ones $(1)$ | tenths $(1 \div 10^1)$ | hundredths $(1 \div 10^2)$ | thousandths $(1 \div 10^3)$ |
|---|---|---|---|---|---|---|
| 1000 meters kilometer | 100 meters hectometer | 10 meters dekameter | 1 meter | $\frac{1}{10}$ meter decimeter | $\frac{1}{100}$ meter centimeter | $\frac{1}{1{,}000}$ meter millimeter |
| | | | 2 | | | |
| | | | 2 | 0 | | |
| | | | 2 | 0 | 0 | |
| | | | 2 | 0 | 0 | 0 |

## Exit Ticket (3 minutes)

After the Student Debrief, instruct students to complete the Exit Ticket. A review of their work will help with assessing students' understanding of the concepts that were presented in today's lesson and planning more effectively for future lessons. The questions may be read aloud to the students.

Lesson 4:     Use exponents to denote powers of 10 with application to metric conversions.

**EUREKA MATH**

Name _____  Date _____

1. Convert and write an equation with an exponent. Use your meter strip when it helps you.

   a.  3 meters to centimeters        3 m = 300 cm          _____ $3 \times 10^2 = 300$ _____

   b.  105 centimeters to meters      105 cm = _____ m      _____

   c.  1.68 meters to centimeters     _____ m = _____ cm   _____

   d.  80 centimeters to meters       _____ cm = _____ m   _____

   e.  9.2 meters to centimeters      _____ m = _____ cm   _____

   f.  4 centimeters to meters        _____ cm = _____ m   _____

   g.  In the space below, list the letters of the problems where larger units are converted to smaller units.

2. Convert using an equation with an exponent. Use your meter strip when it helps you.

   a.  3 meters to millimeters        _____ m = _____ mm    _____

   b.  1.2 meters to millimeters      _____ m = _____ mm    _____

   c.  1,020 millimeters to meters    _____ mm = _____ m    _____

   d.  97 millimeters to meters       _____ mm = _____ m    _____

   e.  7.28 meters to millimeters     _____ m = _____ mm    _____

   f.  4 millimeters to meters        _____ mm = _____ m    _____

   g.  In the space below, list the letters of the problems where smaller units are converted to larger units.

EUREKA
MATH®

Lesson 4:    Use exponents to denote powers of 10 with application to metric
             conversions.

69

3.  Read each aloud as you write the equivalent measures. Write an equation with an exponent you might use to convert.

    a.  3.512 m = _____ mm          $3.512 \times 10^3 = 3{,}512$

    b.  8 cm = _____ m              _____

    c.  42 mm = _____ m             _____

    d.  0.05 m = _____ mm           _____

    e.  0.002 m = _____ cm          _____

4.  The length of the bar for a high jump competition must always be 4.75 m. Express this measurement in millimeters. Explain your thinking. Include an equation with an exponent in your explanation.

5.  A honey bee's length measures 1 cm. Express this measurement in meters. Explain your thinking. Include an equation with an exponent in your explanation.

6.  Explain why converting from meters to centimeters uses a different exponent than converting from meters to millimeters.

Lesson 4:   Use exponents to denote powers of 10 with application to metric conversions.

EUREKA
MATH

Name _____   Date _____

1.  Convert using an equation with an exponent.

    a.  2 meters to centimeters        2 m = _____ cm        _____

    b.  40 millimeters to meters       40 mm = _____ m       _____

2.  Read each aloud as you write the equivalent measures.

    a.  A piece of fabric measures 3.9 meters. Express this length in centimeters.

    b.  Ms. Ramos's thumb measures 4 centimeters. Express this length in meters.

**Lesson 4:**   Use exponents to denote powers of 10 with application to metric
conversions.

© 2015 Great Minds. eureka-math.org
G5-M1-TE-B1-1.3.1-1.2016

71

Name _____     Date _____

1.  Convert and write an equation with an exponent. Use your meter strip when it helps you.

    a.  2 meters to centimeters        2m = 200 cm            _____$2 \times 10^2 = 200$_____

    b.  108 centimeters to meters      108 cm = _____ m      _____

    c.  2.49 meters to centimeters     _____ m = _____ cm  _____

    d.  50 centimeters to meters       _____ cm = _____ m  _____

    e.  6.3 meters to centimeters      _____ m = _____ cm  _____

    f.  7 centimeters to meters        _____ cm = _____ m  _____

    g.  In the space below, list the letters of the problems where smaller units are converted to larger units.

2.  Convert using an equation with an exponent. Use your meter strip when it helps you.

    a.  4 meters to millimeters         _____ m = _____ mm   _____

    b.  1.7 meters to millimeters       _____ m = _____ mm   _____

    c.  1,050 millimeters to meters     _____ mm = _____ m   _____

    d.  65 millimeters to meters        _____ mm = _____ m   _____

    e.  4.92 meters to millimeters      _____ m = _____ mm   _____

    f.  3 millimeters to meters         _____ mm = _____ m   _____

    g.  In the space below, list the letters of the problems where larger units are converted to smaller units.

Lesson 4:    Use exponents to denote powers of 10 with application to metric conversions.

© 2015 Great Minds. eureka-math.org
G5-M1-TE-B1-1.3.1-1.2016

EUREKA
MATH

3.  Read each aloud as you write the equivalent measures. Write an equation with an exponent you might use to convert.

    a.  2.638 m    = _____ mm    <u>    $2.638 \times 10^3 = 2,638$    </u>

    b.  7 cm    = _____ m    _____

    c.  39 mm    = _____ m    _____

    d.  0.08 m    = _____ mm    _____

    e.  0.005 m    = _____ cm    _____

4.  Yi Ting's height is 1.49 m. Express this measurement in millimeters. Explain your thinking. Include an equation with an exponent in your explanation.

5.  A ladybug's length measures 2 cm. Express this measurement in meters. Explain your thinking. Include an equation with an exponent in your explanation.

6.  The length of a sticky note measures 77 millimeters. Express this length in meters. Explain your thinking. Include an equation with an exponent in your explanation.

EUREKA MATH®

Lesson 4:    Use exponents to denote powers of 10 with application to metric conversions.

73

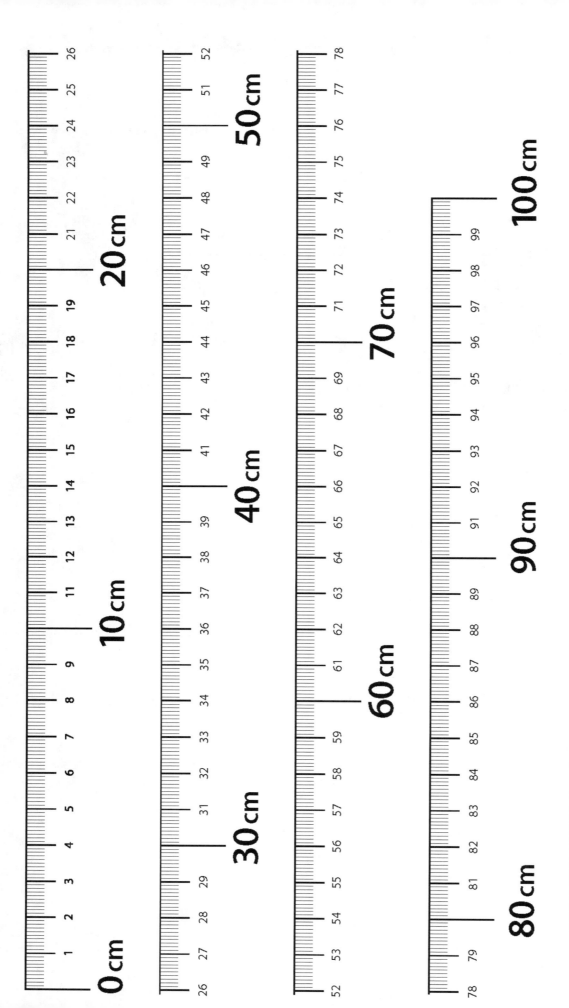

meter strip

**Lesson 4:** Use exponents to denote powers of 10 with application to metric conversions.

© 2015 Great Minds. eureka-math.org
G5-M1-TE-B1-1.3.1-1.2016

**EUREKA MATH**

# Mathematics Curriculum

## Topic B

# Decimal Fractions and Place Value Patterns

### 5.NBT.3

| Focus Standard: | 5.NBT.3 | Read, write, and compare decimals to thousandths. |
|---|---|---|
| | a. | Read and write decimals to thousandths using base-ten numerals, number names, and expanded form, e.g., $347.392 = 3 \times 100 + 4 \times 10 + 7 \times 1 + 3 \times (1/10) + 9 \times (1/100) + 2 \times (1/1000)$. |
| | b. | Compare two decimals to thousandths based on meanings of the digits in each place, using >, =, and < symbols to record the results of comparisons. |
| Instructional Days: | 2 | |
| Coherence   -Links from: | G4–M1 | Place Value, Rounding, and Algorithms for Addition and Subtraction |
| -Links to: | G6–M2 | Arithmetic Operations Including Dividing by a Fraction |

Naming decimal fractions in expanded, unit, and word forms in order to compare decimal fractions is the focus of Topic B (**5.NBT.3**). Familiar methods of expressing expanded form are used, but students are also encouraged to apply their knowledge of exponents to expanded forms (e.g., $4,300.01 = 4 \times 10^3 + 3 \times 10^2 + 1 \times 1/100$). Place value charts and disks offer a beginning for comparing decimal fractions to the thousandths but are quickly supplanted by reasoning about the meaning of the digits in each place, noticing differences in the values of like units and expressing those comparisons with symbols (>, <, and =).

| A Teaching Sequence Toward Mastery of Decimal Fractions and Place Value Patterns |
|---|
| **Objective 1: Name decimal fractions in expanded, unit, and word forms by applying place value reasoning.**<br>**(Lesson 5)** |
| **Objective 2: Compare decimal fractions to the thousandths using like units, and express comparisons with >, <, =.**<br>**(Lesson 6)** |

# Lesson 5

Objective: Name decimal fractions in expanded, unit, and word forms by applying place value reasoning.

## Suggested Lesson Structure

■ Fluency Practice          (12 minutes)
■ Application Problem        (8 minutes)
■ Concept Development       (30 minutes)
■ Student Debrief           (10 minutes)
   **Total Time**          **(60 minutes)**

## Fluency Practice  (12 minutes)

- Sprint:  Multiply Decimals by 10, 100, and 1,000  **5.NBT.2**     (8 minutes)
- Multiply and Divide by Exponents  **5.NBT.2**                     (2 minutes)
- Multiply Metric Units  **5.MD.1**                                  (2 minutes)

### Sprint:  Multiply Decimals by 10, 100, and 1,000  (8 minutes)

Materials:   (S) Multiply Decimals by 10, 100, and 1,000 Sprint

Note:  This Sprint helps students work toward automaticity of multiplying and dividing decimals by 10, 100, and 1,000.

### Multiply and Divide by Exponents  (2 minutes)

Materials:   (S) Millions to thousandths place value chart (Lesson 1 Template), personal white board

Note:  This fluency activity helps students work toward mastery of the concept introduced in Lesson 4.

Depending on students' depth of knowledge, this activity may be done with support from a personal place value chart or done simply by responding on the personal white board with the product or quotient.

- T:  (Project the place value chart from millions to thousandths.) Write 54 tenths as a decimal.
- S:  (Write 5 in the ones column and 4 in the tenths column.)
- T:  Say the decimal.
- S:  5.4 (five and four tenths).
- T:  Multiply it by $10^2$.
- S:  (Indicate change in value by using arrows from each original place value to the product on their personal white boards. Or, instead, simply write the product.)

---

Lesson 5:      Name decimal fractions in expanded, unit, and word forms by
                                    applying place value reasoning.

T: Say the product.

S: 540.

Repeat the process and sequence for $0.6 \times 10^2$, $0.6 \div 10^2$, $2.784 \times 10^3$, and $6,583 \div 10^3$.

## Multiplying Metric Units  (2 minutes)

Materials:  (S) Millions to thousandths place value chart (Lesson 1 Template), personal white board

Note:  This fluency activity helps students work toward mastery of the concept introduced in Lesson 4.

T: (Write 3 m = ____ cm.) Show 3 on your place value chart.

S: (Write 3 in the ones column.)

T: How many centimeters are in 1 meter?

S: 100 centimeters.

T: Show how many centimeters are in 3 meters on your place value chart.

S: (Cross out the 3, and shift it two place values to the left to show 300.)

T: How many centimeters are in 3 meters?

S: 300 centimeters.

Repeat the process and procedure for 7 kg = ____ g, 7,000 mL = ____ L, 7,500 m = ____ km ____ m, and 8,350 g = ____ kg ____ g.

## Application Problem  (8 minutes)

Jordan measures a desk at 200 cm. James measures the same desk in millimeters, and Amy measures the same desk in meters. What is James's measurement in millimeters? What is Amy's measurement in meters? Show your thinking using a place value chart or an equation with exponents.

Note:  Today's Application Problem offers students a quick review of yesterday's concepts before moving forward to naming decimals.

James:  $200 \times 10^1 = 2,000$
200 cm = 2,000 mm

Amy:  $200 \div 10^2 = 2$
200 cm = 2 m

## Concept Development  (30 minutes)

Materials:  (S) Personal white board, thousands through thousandths place value chart (Template)

**Opener**

T: (Write *three thousand forty-seven* on the board.) On your personal board, write this number in standard form, expanded form, and unit form.

T: Explain to your partner the purpose of writing this number in these different forms.

S: Standard form shows us the digits that we are using to represent that amount. → Expanded form shows how much each digit is worth and that the number is a total of those values added together. → Unit form helps us see how many of each size unit are in the number.

Lesson 5:    Name decimal fractions in expanded, unit, and word forms by applying place value reasoning.

77

## Problem 1

Represent 1 thousandth and 3 thousandths in standard, expanded, and unit form.

T:   Write 1 thousandth using digits on your place value chart.

T:   How many ones, tenths, hundredths, thousandths?

S:   Zero. Zero. Zero. One.

T:   This is the standard form of the decimal for 1 thousandth.

T:   We write 1 thousandth as a fraction like this: $\frac{1}{1000}$. (Write $\frac{1}{1000}$ on the board.)

T:   1 thousandth is a single copy of a thousandth. We write the expanded form using a fraction like this: $1 \times \left(\frac{1}{1000}\right)$. (Write $1 \times \frac{1}{1000}$ on the board, and say *1 copy of 1 thousandth*.) And, we write the expanded form using a decimal like this: $1 \times 0.001$. (Write $1 \times 0.001$ on the board.)

T:   We write the unit form of 1 thousandth like this: 1 thousandth. (Write on the board.) We write a numeral (point to 1) and the unit name (point to thousandth) as a word.

> One thousandth = $0.001$ = $\frac{1}{1000}$
>
> $\frac{1}{1000} = 1 \times \left(\frac{1}{1000}\right)$
>
> $0.001 = 1 \times 0.001$
>
> 1 thousandth

T:   Imagine 3 copies of 1 thousandth. How many thousandths is that?

S:   3 thousandths.

T:   (Write in standard form and as a fraction.)

T:   3 thousandths is 3 copies of 1 thousandth. Turn and talk to your partner about how this would be written in expanded form using a fraction and using a decimal.

> Three thousandths = $0.003$ = $\frac{3}{1000}$
>
> $\frac{3}{1000} = 3 \times \left(\frac{1}{1000}\right)$
>
> $0.003 = 3 \times 0.001$
>
> 3 thousandths

## Problem 2

Represent 13 thousandths in standard, expanded, and unit form.

T:   Write 13 thousandths in standard form and expanded form using fractions and then using decimals. Turn and share with your partner.

S:   *Zero point zero one three* is standard form. Expanded forms are $1 \times \left(\frac{1}{100}\right) + 3 \times \left(\frac{1}{1000}\right)$ and $1 \times 0.01 + 3 \times 0.001$.

Lesson 5:    Name decimal fractions in expanded, unit, and word forms by applying place value reasoning.

EUREKA MATH

T:  Now, write this decimal in unit form.

S:  1 hundredth 3 thousandths → 13 thousandths.

T:  (Circulate and write responses on the board.) I notice that there seems to be more than one way to write this decimal in unit form. Why?

S:  This is 13 copies of 1 thousandth. → You can write the units separately or write the 1 hundredth as 10 thousandths. You add 10 thousandths and 3 thousandths to get 13 thousandths.

NOTES ON
MULTIPLE MEANS
OF ENGAGEMENT:

Students struggling with naming decimals using different unit forms may benefit from a return to concrete materials. Try using place value disks to make trades for smaller units. Also, place value understandings from Lessons 1 and 2 help make the connection between 1 hundredth 3 thousandths and 13 thousandths.

It may also be fruitful to invite students to extend their Grade 4 experiences with finding equivalent fractions for tenths and hundredths to finding equivalent fraction representations in thousandths.

$$\text{Thirteen thousandths} = 0.013 = \frac{13}{1000}$$

$$\frac{13}{1000} = 13 \times \left(\frac{1}{1000}\right)$$

$$0.013 = 1 \times 0.01 + 3 \times 0.001$$

1 hundredth 3 thousandths

13 thousandths

Repeat with 0.273 and 1.608, allowing students to combine units in their unit forms (e.g., 2 tenths 73 thousandths, 273 thousandths, 27 hundredths 3 thousandths). Use more or fewer examples as needed, reminding students who need it that *and* indicates the decimal in word form.

**Problem 3**

Represent 25.413 in word, expanded, and unit form.

T:  (Write 25.413 on the board.) Write 25.413 in word form on your personal board.

S:  (Write twenty-five and four hundred thirteen thousandths.)

T:  Now, write this decimal in unit form on your personal board.

S:  (Write 2 tens 5 ones 4 tenths 1 hundredth 3 thousandths.)

T:  What are other unit forms of this number?

S:  25 ones 413 thousandths. → 254 tenths 13 hundredths. → 25,413 thousandths.

T:  Write 25.413 as a mixed number and then in expanded form. Compare your work with your partner's.

$$\text{Twenty-five and four hundred thirteen thousandths} = 25\frac{413}{1000} = 25.413$$

$$25\frac{413}{1000} = 2 \times 10 + 5 \times 1 + 4 \times \left(\frac{1}{10}\right) + 1 \times \left(\frac{1}{100}\right) + 3 \times \left(\frac{1}{1000}\right)$$

$$25.413 = 2 \times 10 + 5 \times 1 + 4 \times 0.1 + 1 \times 0.01 + 3 \times 0.001$$

2 tens 5 ones 4 tenths 1 hundredth 3 thousandths

25 ones 413 thousandths

Repeat the sequence with 12.04 and 9.495. Use more or fewer examples as needed.

© 2015 Great Minds. eureka-math.org
G5-M1-TE-B1-1.3.1-1.2016

### Problem 4

Write the standard, expanded, and unit forms of *four hundred four thousandths* and *four hundred and four thousandths.*

- T: Work with your partner to write these decimals in standard form. (Circulate. Look for misconceptions about the use of the word *and.*)
- T: Tell the digits you used to write *four hundred four thousandths.*
- T: How did you know where to write the decimal in the standard form?
- S: The word *and* tells us where the fraction part of the number starts.
- T: Now, work with your partner to write the expanded and unit forms for these numbers.

**NOTES ON MULTIPLE MEANS OF REPRESENTATION:**

Guide students to draw on their past experiences with whole numbers and make parallels to decimals. Whole number units are named by smallest base thousand unit (e.g., 365,000 = 365 thousand and 365 = 365 ones). Likewise, we can name decimals by the smallest unit (e.g., 0.63 = 63 hundredths).

$$\text{Four hundred four thousandths} = \frac{404}{1000} = 0.404$$

$$\frac{404}{1000} = 4 \times \left(\frac{1}{10}\right) + 4 \times \left(\frac{1}{1000}\right)$$

$$0.404 = 4 \times 0.1 + 4 \times 0.001$$

4 tenths 4 thousandths

$$\text{Four hundred and four thousandths} = 400 \frac{4}{1000} =$$

$$400.004 \quad 400 \frac{4}{1000} = 4 \times 100 + 4 \times \left(\frac{1}{1000}\right)$$

$$400.004 = 4 \times 100 + 4 \times 0.001$$

4 hundreds 4 thousandths

Repeat this sequence with *two hundred two thousandths* and *nine hundred and nine tenths.*

- T: Work on your Problem Set now. Read the word forms carefully!

## Problem Set  (10 minutes)

Students should do their personal best to complete the Problem Set within the allotted 10 minutes. For some classes, it may be appropriate to modify the assignment by specifying which problems they work on first. Some problems do not specify a method for solving. Students solve these problems using the RDW approach used for Application Problems.

Lesson 5:   Name decimal fractions in expanded, unit, and word forms by applying place value reasoning.

EUREKA MATH

# Student Debrief (10 minutes)

**Lesson Objective:** Name decimal fractions in expanded, unit, and word forms by applying place value reasoning.

The Student Debrief is intended to invite reflection and active processing of the total lesson experience.

Invite students to review their solutions for the Problem Set. They should check work by comparing answers with a partner before going over answers as a class. Look for misconceptions or misunderstandings that can be addressed in the Debrief. Guide students in a conversation to debrief the Problem Set and process the lesson.

Any combination of the questions below may be used to lead the discussion.

- Which tasks in Problem 1 are alike? Why?
- What is the purpose of writing a decimal number in expanded form using fractions? What was the objective of our lesson today?
- Compare your answers to Problem 1(d) and 1(e). What is the importance of the word *and* when naming decimals in standard form?
- When might expanded form be useful as a calculation tool? (It helps us see the like units and could help to add and subtract mentally.)
- How is expanded form related to the standard form of a number?

# Exit Ticket (3 minutes)

After the Student Debrief, instruct students to complete the Exit Ticket. A review of their work will help with assessing students' understanding of the concepts that were presented in today's lesson and planning more effectively for future lessons. The questions may be read aloud to the students.

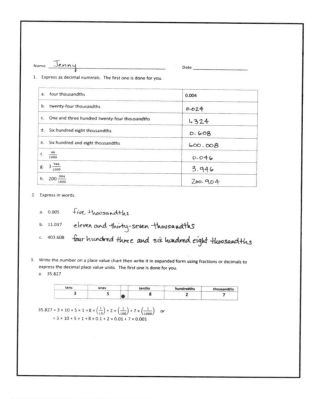

EUREKA MATH®

Lesson 5: Name decimal fractions in expanded, unit, and word forms by applying place value reasoning.

81

© 2015 Great Minds. eureka-math.org
G5-M1-TE-B1-1.3.1-1.2016

# A

Number Correct: _____

Multiply Decimals by 10, 100, and 1,000

| | | |
|---|---|---|
| 1. | 62.3 × 10 = | |
| 2. | 62.3 × 100 = | |
| 3. | 62.3 × 1,000 = | |
| 4. | 73.6 × 10 = | |
| 5. | 73.6 × 100 = | |
| 6. | 73.6 × 1,000 = | |
| 7. | 0.6 × 10 = | |
| 8. | 0.06 × 10 = | |
| 9. | 0.006 × 10 = | |
| 10. | 0.3 × 10 = | |
| 11. | 0.3 × 100 = | |
| 12. | 0.3 × 1,000 = | |
| 13. | 0.02 × 10 = | |
| 14. | 0.02 × 100 = | |
| 15. | 0.02 × 1,000 = | |
| 16. | 0.008 × 10 = | |
| 17. | 0.008 × 100 = | |
| 18. | 0.008 × 1,000 = | |
| 19. | 0.32 × 10 = | |
| 20. | 0.67 × 10 = | |
| 21. | 0.91 × 100 = | |
| 22. | 0.74 × 100 = | |

| | | |
|---|---|---|
| 23. | 4.1 × 1,000 = | |
| 24. | 7.6 × 1,000 = | |
| 25. | 0.01 × 1,000 = | |
| 26. | 0.07 × 1,000 = | |
| 27. | 0.072 × 100 = | |
| 28. | 0.802 × 10 = | |
| 29. | 0.019 × 1,000 = | |
| 30. | 7.412 × 1,000 = | |
| 31. | 6.8 × 100 = | |
| 32. | 4.901 × 10 = | |
| 33. | 16.07 × 100 = | |
| 34. | 9.19 × 10 = | |
| 35. | 18.2 × 100 = | |
| 36. | 14.7 × 1,000 = | |
| 37. | 2.021 × 100 = | |
| 38. | 172.1 × 10 = | |
| 39. | 3.2 × 20 = | |
| 40. | 4.1 × 20 = | |
| 41. | 3.2 × 30 = | |
| 42. | 1.3 × 30 = | |
| 43. | 3.12 × 40 = | |
| 44. | 14.12 × 40 = | |

Lesson 5:    Name decimal fractions in expanded, unit, and word forms by applying place value reasoning.

**EUREKA MATH**

# B

Number Correct: _____

Improvement: _____

Multiply Decimals by 10, 100, and 1,000

| | | |
|---|---|---|
| 1. | 46.1 × 10 = | |
| 2. | 46.1 × 100 = | |
| 3. | 46.1 × 1,000 = | |
| 4. | 89.2 × 10 = | |
| 5. | 89.2 × 100 = | |
| 6. | 89.2 × 1,000 = | |
| 7. | 0.3 × 10 = | |
| 8. | 0.03 × 10 = | |
| 9. | 0.003 × 10 = | |
| 10. | 0.9 × 10 = | |
| 11. | 0.9 × 100 = | |
| 12. | 0.9 × 1,000 = | |
| 13. | 0.04 × 10 = | |
| 14. | 0.04 × 100 = | |
| 15. | 0.04 × 1,000 = | |
| 16. | 0.007 × 10 = | |
| 17. | 0.007 × 100 = | |
| 18. | 0.007 × 1,000 = | |
| 19. | 0.45 × 10 = | |
| 20. | 0.78 × 10 = | |
| 21. | 0.28 × 100 = | |
| 22. | 0.19 × 100 = | |

| | | |
|---|---|---|
| 23. | 5.2 × 1,000 = | |
| 24. | 8.7 × 1,000 = | |
| 25. | 0.01 × 1,000 = | |
| 26. | 0.08 × 1,000 = | |
| 27. | 0.083 × 10 = | |
| 28. | 0.903 × 10 = | |
| 29. | 0.017 × 1,000 = | |
| 30. | 8.523 × 1,000 = | |
| 31. | 7.9 × 100 = | |
| 32. | 5.802 × 10 = | |
| 33. | 27.08 × 100 = | |
| 34. | 8.18 × 10 = | |
| 35. | 29.3 × 100 = | |
| 36. | 25.8 × 1,000 = | |
| 37. | 3.032 × 100 = | |
| 38. | 283.1 × 10 = | |
| 39. | 2.1 × 20 = | |
| 40. | 3.3 × 20 = | |
| 41. | 3.1 × 30 = | |
| 42. | 1.2 × 30 = | |
| 43. | 2.11 × 40 = | |
| 44. | 13.11 × 40 = | |

Lesson 5:     Name decimal fractions in expanded, unit, and word forms by
              applying place value reasoning.

83

© 2015 Great Minds. eureka-math.org
G5-M1-TE-B1-1.3.1-1.2016

Name _____  Date _____

1. Express as decimal numerals. The first one is done for you.

| | | |
|---|---|---|
| a. | Four thousandths | 0.004 |
| b. | Twenty-four thousandths | |
| c. | One and three hundred twenty-four thousandths | |
| d. | Six hundred eight thousandths | |
| e. | Six hundred and eight thousandths | |
| f. | $\frac{46}{1000}$ | |
| g. | $3\frac{946}{1000}$ | |
| h. | $200\frac{904}{1000}$ | |

2. Express each of the following values in words.

   a.  0.005    _____

   b.  11.037   _____

   c.  403.608  _____

3. Write the number on a place value chart. Then, write it in expanded form using fractions or decimals to express the decimal place value units. The first one is done for you.

   a.  35.827

| Tens | Ones | | Tenths | Hundredths | Thousandths |
|---|---|---|---|---|---|
| 3 | 5 | ● | 8 | 2 | 7 |

$$35.827 = 3 \times 10 + 5 \times 1 + 8 \times \left(\frac{1}{10}\right) + 2 \times \left(\frac{1}{100}\right) + 7 \times \left(\frac{1}{1000}\right) \ or$$
$$= 3 \times 10 + 5 \times 1 + 8 \times 0.1 + 2 \times 0.01 + 7 \times 0.001$$

Lesson 5:    Name decimal fractions in expanded, unit, and word forms by applying place value reasoning.

b. 0.249

c. 57.281

4. Write a decimal for each of the following. Use a place value chart to help, if necessary.

   a. $7 \times 10 + 4 \times 1 + 6 \times \left(\frac{1}{10}\right) + 9 \times \left(\frac{1}{100}\right) + 2 \times \left(\frac{1}{1000}\right)$

   b. $5 \times 100 + 3 \times 10 + 8 \times 0.1 + 9 \times 0.001$

   c. $4 \times 1{,}000 + 2 \times 100 + 7 \times 1 + 3 \times \left(\frac{1}{100}\right) + 4 \times \left(\frac{1}{1000}\right)$

5. Mr. Pham wrote 2.619 on the board. Christy says it is two and six hundred nineteen thousandths. Amy says it is 2 ones 6 tenths 1 hundredth 9 thousandths. Who is right? Use words and numbers to explain your answer.

EUREKA MATH

Lesson 5: Name decimal fractions in expanded, unit, and word forms by applying place value reasoning.

85

© 2015 Great Minds. eureka-math.org
G5-M1-TE-B1-1.3.1-1.2016

Name _____   Date _____

1.  Express nine thousandths as a decimal.

2.  Express twenty-nine thousandths as a fraction.

3.  Express 24.357 in words.

    a.  Write the expanded form using fractions or decimals.

    b.  Express in unit form.

**Lesson 5:**   Name decimal fractions in expanded, unit, and word forms by
applying place value reasoning.

© 2015 Great Minds. eureka-math.org
G5-M1-TE-B1-1.3.1-1.2016

**EUREKA
MATH**

Name _____ Date _____

1. Express as decimal numerals. The first one is done for you.

| | | |
|---|---|---|
| a. | Five thousandths | 0.005 |
| b. | Thirty-five thousandths | |
| c. | Nine and two hundred thirty-five thousandths | |
| d. | Eight hundred and five thousandths | |
| e. | $\frac{8}{1000}$ | |
| f. | $\frac{28}{1000}$ | |
| g. | $7\frac{528}{1000}$ | |
| h. | $300\frac{502}{1000}$ | |

2. Express each of the following values in words.

   a. 0.008  _____

   b. 15.062  _____

   c. 607.409 _____

3. Write the number on a place value chart. Then, write it in expanded form using fractions or decimals to express the decimal place value units. The first one is done for you.

   a. 27.346

| Tens | Ones | | Tenths | Hundredths | Thousandths |
|---|---|---|---|---|---|
| 2 | 7 | ● | 3 | 4 | 6 |

$$27.346 = 2 \times 10 + 7 \times 1 + 3 \times \left(\frac{1}{10}\right) + 4 \times \left(\frac{1}{100}\right) + 6 \times \left(\frac{1}{1000}\right) \ or$$
$$27.346 = 2 \times 10 + 7 \times 1 + 3 \times 0.1 + 4 \times 0.01 + 6 \times 0.001$$

**EUREKA MATH**

Lesson 5:    Name decimal fractions in expanded, unit, and word forms by applying place value reasoning.

87

© 2015 Great Minds. eureka-math.org
G5-M1-TE-B1-1.3.1-1.2016

    b.   0.362

    c.   49.564

4. Write a decimal for each of the following. Use a place value chart to help, if necessary.

    a.  $3 \times 10 + 5 \times 1 + 2 \times \left(\frac{1}{10}\right) + 7 \times \left(\frac{1}{100}\right) + 6 \times \left(\frac{1}{1000}\right)$

    b.  $9 \times 100 + 2 \times 10 + 3 \times 0.1 + 7 \times 0.001$

    c.  $5 \times 1000 + 4 \times 100 + 8 \times 1 + 6 \times \left(\frac{1}{100}\right) + 5 \times \left(\frac{1}{1000}\right)$

5. At the beginning of a lesson, a piece of chalk is 4.875 inches long. At the end of the lesson, it is 3.125 inches long. Write the two amounts in expanded form using fractions.

    a.   At the beginning of the lesson:

    b.   At the end of the lesson:

6. Mrs. Herman asked the class to write an expanded form for 412.638. Nancy wrote the expanded form using fractions, and Charles wrote the expanded form using decimals. Write their responses.

Lesson 5:   Name decimal fractions in expanded, unit, and word forms by applying place value reasoning.

EUREKA MATH

© 2015 Great Minds. eureka-math.org
G5-M1-TE-B1-1.3.1-1.2016

| Thousands | Hundreds | Tens | Ones | Tenths | Hundredths | Thousandths |
|---|---|---|---|---|---|---|
| | | | | | | |

thousands through thousandths place value chart

Lesson 5:   Name decimal fractions in expanded, unit, and word forms by
applying place value reasoning.

89

© 2015 Great Minds. eureka-math.org
G5-M1-TE-B1-1.3.1-1.2016

# Lesson 6

Objective:  Compare decimal fractions to the thousandths using like units, and express comparisons with >, <, =.

## Suggested Lesson Structure

■ Fluency Practice          (12 minutes)
▧ Application Problem        (8 minutes)
▨ Concept Development        (30 minutes)
■ Student Debrief           (10 minutes)
  **Total Time**            **(60 minutes)**

## Fluency Practice  (12 minutes)

- Find the Midpoint  **5.NBT.4**                (5 minutes)
- Rename the Units  **5.NBT.1**                 (2 minutes)
- Multiply by Decimal Fractions  **5.NBT.3a**   (5 minutes)

### Find the Midpoint  (5 minutes)

Materials:   (S) Personal white board

Note:  Practicing this skill in isolation helps students conceptually understand rounding decimals in Lesson 12.

T:  (Draw a 0 on the left side of a number line and 10 on the right side of the number line.) What's halfway between 0 ones and 10 ones?

S:  5 ones.

T:  (Write 5 ones halfway between the 0 and 10. Draw a second number line directly beneath the first. Write 0 on the left side and 1 on the right side.) How many tenths is 1?

S:  1 is 10 tenths.

T:  (Write 10 tenths below the 1.) On your boards, write the decimal that is halfway between 0 and 1 or 10 tenths.

S:  (Write 0.5 approximately halfway between 0 and 1 on their number lines.)

Repeat the process for these possible sequences: 0 and 0.1, 0 and 0.01, 10 and 20, 1 and 2, 0.1 and 0.2, 0.01 and 0.02, 0.7 and 0.8, 0.7 and 0.71, 9 and 10, 0.9 and 1, and 0.09 and 0.1.

**Lesson 6:**     Compare decimal fractions to the thousandths using like units, and
                      express comparisons with >, <, =.

## Rename the Units  (2 minutes)

Note:  Reviewing unit conversions helps students work toward mastery of decomposing common units into compound units.

  T:   (Write 100 cm = _____ m.) Rename the units.
  S:   100 cm = 1 meter.
  T:   (Write 200 cm = _____ m.) Rename the units.
  S:   200 centimeters = 2 meters.
  T:   700 centimeters.
  S:   7 meters.
  T:   (Write 750 cm = _____ m _____ cm.) Rename the units.
  S:   7 meters 50 centimeters.

Repeat the process for 450 cm, 630 cm, and 925 cm.

## Multiply by Decimal Fractions  (5 minutes)

Materials:   (S) Personal white board, millions to thousandths place value chart (Lesson 1 Template)

Note:  Reviewing the concept helps students work toward mastery of this skill introduced in previous lessons.

  T:   (Project a place value chart from tens to thousandths. Beneath the chart, write 3 × 10 = _____.) Say the multiplication sentence.
  S:   3 × 10 = 30.
  T:   (Write 3 in the tens column. Below the multiplication sentence, write 30. To the right of 3 × 10, write 4 × 1 = _____.) Say the multiplication sentence.
  S:   4 × 1 = 4.
  T:   (Write 4 in the ones column, and fill in the addition sentence so that it reads 30 + 4.)

Repeat the process with each of the expressions below so that, in the end, the number 34.652 will be written in the place value chart and 30 + 4 + 0.6 + 0.05 + 0.002 is written underneath it:

$$6 \times \frac{1}{10} \qquad\qquad 5 \times \frac{1}{100} \qquad\qquad 2 \times \frac{1}{1000}$$

  T:   Say the addition sentence.
  S:   30 + 4 + 0.6 + 0.05 + 0.002 = 34.652.
  T:   (Write 75.614 on the place value chart.) Write the number in expanded form.

Repeat with the following possible sequence: 75.604, 20.197, and 40.803.

## Application Problem  (8 minutes)

Ms. Meyer measured the edge of her dining table to the hundredths of a meter. The edge of the table measured 32.15 meters. Write her measurement in word form, unit form, and expanded form using fractions and decimals.

Encourage students to name the decimal by decomposing it into various units (e.g., 3,215 hundredths; 321 tenths 5 hundredths; 32 ones 15 hundredths).

*32.15 meters*

*Word form:*
*Thirty-two and fifteen hundredth*

*Unit form:*
*3 tens, 2 ones, 1 tenth, 5 hundredths*

*Expanded form:*
*30 + 2 + 0.1 + 0.05*
$30 + 2 + \frac{1}{10} + \frac{5}{100}$

EUREKA
MATH®

Lesson 6:   Compare decimal fractions to the thousandths using like units, and
            express comparisons with >, <, =.

91

© 2015 Great Minds. eureka-math.org
G5-M1-TE-B1-1.3.1-1.2016

## Concept Development  (30 minutes)

Materials:    (S) Millions to thousands place value chart (Lesson 1 Template), personal white board

**Problem 1**

Compare 13,196 and 13,296.

MP.2

- T:  (Point to 13,196.) Read the number.
- S:  13 thousand, 1 hundred ninety-six.
- T:  (Point to 13,296.) Read the number.
- S:  13 thousand, 2 hundred ninety-six.
- T:  Which number is greater? How can you tell?
- S:  13,296 is greater than 13,196 because the digit in the hundreds place is one greater. → 13,296 is 100 more than 13,196. → 13,196 has 131 hundreds and 13,296 has 132 hundreds, so 13,296 is greater.
- T:  Use a symbol to show which number is greater.
- S:  13,196 < 13,296.

**Problem 2**

Compare 0.012 and 0.002.

- T:  Write 2 thousandths in standard form on your place value chart. (Write 2 thousandths on the board.)
- S:  (Write.)
- T:  Say the digits that you wrote on your chart.
- S:  Zero point zero zero two.
- T:  Write 12 thousandths in standard form underneath 0.002 on your chart. (Write 12 thousandths on the board.)
- S:  (Write.)
- T:  Say the digits that you wrote on your chart.
- S:  Zero point zero one two.
- T:  Say this number in unit form.
- S:  1 hundredth 2 thousandths.
- T:  Which number is greater? Turn and talk to your partner about how you can tell.
- S:  0.012 is bigger than 0.002. → In 0.012, there is a one in the hundredths place, but 0.002 has a zero in the hundredths, so that means 0.012 is greater than 0.002. → 12 of something is greater than 2 of the same thing. Just like 12 apples are more than 2 apples.
- T:  Write an expression comparing these two values.
- S:  0.002 < 0.012.

---

**Lesson 6:**     Compare decimal fractions to the thousandths using like units, and express comparisons with >, <, =.

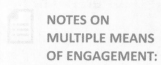

### Problem 3

Compare $\frac{299}{1000}$ and $\frac{3}{10}$.

T: Write 3 tenths in standard form on your place value chart.

S: (Write.)

T: Write 299 thousandths in standard form on your place value chart under 3 tenths.

S: (Write.)

T: Which decimal has more tenths?

S: 0.3.

T: If we traded 3 tenths for thousandths, how many thousandths would we need? Turn and talk to your partner.

S: 300 thousandths.

T: Name these decimals using unit form and compare. Tell your partner which is greater.

**MP.4**

S: 299 thousandths. 300 thousandths is more.

T: Show this relationship with a symbol.

S: 0.299 < 0.3.

Repeat the sequence with $\frac{705}{1000}$ and $\frac{7}{10}$ and 15.203 and 15.21.

Encourage students to name the fractions and decimals using like units as above (e.g., 15 ones 20 tenths 3 thousandths and 15 ones 21 tenths 0 hundredths or 15,203 thousandths and 15,210 thousandths). Be sure to have students express the relationships using <, >, and =.

**NOTES ON MULTIPLE MEANS OF ENGAGEMENT:**

Help students deepen their understanding of comparing decimals by returning to concrete materials. Some students may not see that 0.4 > 0.399 because they are focusing on the number of digits to the right of the decimal rather than their value. Comparison of like units becomes a concrete experience when students' attention is directed to comparisons of largest to smallest place value on the chart and when they are encouraged to make trades to the smaller unit using disks.

**NOTES ON MULTIPLE MEANS OF ENGAGEMENT:**

Provide an extension by including fractions along with decimals to be ordered.

Order from least to greatest: 29.5, 27.019, and $27\frac{5}{1000}$.

### Problem 4

Order from least to greatest: 0.413, 0.056, 0.164, and 0.531.

Have students order the decimals and then explain their strategy (e.g., renaming in unit form, using a place value chart to compare largest to smallest units looking for differences in value).

Repeat with the following in ascending and descending order: 27.005, 29.04, 27.019, and 29.5; 119.177, 119.173, 119.078, and 119.18.

## Problem Set  (10 minutes)

Students should do their personal best to complete the problem set within the allotted 10 minutes. For some classes, it may be appropriate to modify the assignment by specifying which problems they work on first. Some problems do not specify a method for solving. Students solve these problems using the RDW approach used for Application Problems.

On this Problem Set, it is suggested that all students begin with Problems 1, 2, and 5 and possibly leave Problems 3 and 6 for the end, if time allows.

Lesson 6:     Compare decimal fractions to the thousandths using like units, and                 93
              express comparisons with >, <, =.

© 2015 Great Minds. eureka-math.org
G5-M1-TE-B1-1.3.1-1.2016

## Student Debrief  (10 minutes)

**Lesson Objective:**  Compare decimal fractions to the thousandths using like units, and express comparisons with >, <, =.

The Student Debrief is intended to invite reflection and active processing of the total lesson experience.

Invite students to review their solutions for the Problem Set. They should check work by comparing answers with a partner before going over answers as a class. Look for misconceptions or misunderstandings that can be addressed in the Debrief. Guide students in a conversation to debrief the Problem Set and process the lesson. Any combination of the questions below may be used to lead the discussion.

- How is comparing whole numbers like comparing decimal fractions? How is it different?

- You learned two strategies to help you compare numbers (finding a common unit and looking at the place value chart). Which strategy do you like best? Explain.

- Allow sufficient time for an in-depth discussion of Problem 5. As these are commonly held misconceptions when comparing decimals, it is worthy of special attention. Ask the following series of questions. What is the mistake that Lance is making? (He's not using like units to compare the numbers. He's forgetting that decimals are named by their smallest units.) How could Angel have named his quantity of water so that the units were the same as Lance's? How would using the same units have helped Lance to make a correct comparison? How is renaming these decimals in the same unit like changing fractions to like denominators?

- Compare 7 tens and 7 tenths. How are they alike? How are they different? (Encourage students to notice that both quantities are 7, but the units have different values.) Also, encourage students to notice that they are placed symmetrically in relation to the ones place on place value chart. Tens are 10 times greater than ones while tenths are 1 tenth as much. Repeat with other values, (e.g., 2000, 0.002), or ask students to generate values that are symmetrically placed on the chart.

## Exit Ticket  (3 minutes)

After the Student Debrief, instruct students to complete the Exit Ticket. A review of their work will help with assessing students' understanding of the concepts that were presented in today's lesson and planning more effectively for future lessons. The questions may be read aloud to the students.

5. Lance measured 0.485 liter of water.  Angel measured 0.5 liter of water.  Lance said, "My beaker has more water than yours because my number has 3 decimal places and yours only has 1."  is Lance correct? Use words and numbers to explain your answer.

Lance is not correct because 5 tenths liter is equal to 500 thousandths liter. 500 thousandths of something is greater than 485 thousandths of something.

$$0.5 > 0.485$$

6. Dr. Hong prescribed 0.019 liter more medicine than Dr. Tannenbaum.  Dr. Evans prescribed 0.02 less than Dr. Hong.  Who prescribed the most medicine?  Who prescribed the least?

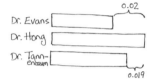

Dr. Evans
Dr. Hong
Dr. Tann-
enbaum

0.02

0.019

Dr. Hong prescribed the most medicine.
Dr. Evans prescribed the least medicine.

Lesson 6:   Compare decimal fractions to the thousandths using like units, and express comparisons with >, <, =.

95

© 2015 Great Minds. eureka-math.org
G5-M1-TE-B1-1.3.1-1.2016

Name _____  Date _____

1. Show the numbers on the place value chart using digits. Use >, <, or = to compare. Explain your thinking in the space to the right.

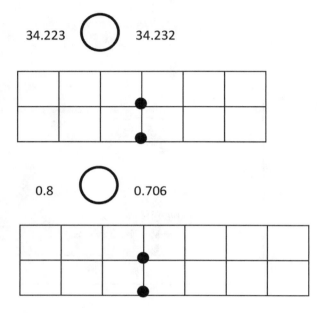

34.223 ◯ 34.232

0.8 ◯ 0.706

2. Use >, <, or = to compare the following. Use a place value chart to help, if necessary.

| | | |
|---|---|---|
| a. 16.3 | ◯ | 16.4 |
| b. 0.83 | ◯ | $\frac{83}{100}$ |
| c. $\frac{205}{1000}$ | ◯ | 0.205 |
| d. 95.580 | ◯ | 95.58 |
| e. 9.1 | ◯ | 9.099 |
| f. 8.3 | ◯ | 83 tenths |
| g. 5.8 | ◯ | Fifty-eight hundredths |

Lesson 6:  Compare decimal fractions to the thousandths using like units, and express comparisons with >, <, =.

© 2015 Great Minds. eureka-math.org
G5-M1-TE-B1-1.3.1-1.2016

EUREKA MATH

| | | |
|---|---|---|
| h. Thirty-six and nine thousandths | ◯ | 4 tens |
| i. 202 hundredths | ◯ | 2 hundreds and 2 thousandths |
| j. One hundred fifty-eight thousandths | ◯ | 158,000 |
| k. 4.15 | ◯ | 415 tenths |

3. Arrange the numbers in increasing order.

   a.  3.049   3.059   3.05   3.04

   _____

   b.  182.205   182.05   182.105   182.025

   _____

4. Arrange the numbers in decreasing order.

   a.  7.608   7.68   7.6   7.068

   _____

   b.  439.216   439.126   439.612   439.261

   _____

Lesson 6:   Compare decimal fractions to the thousandths using like units, and express comparisons with >, <, =.

5.  Lance measured 0.485 liter of water. Angel measured 0.5 liter of water. Lance said, "My beaker has more water than yours because my number has three decimal places and yours only has one." Is Lance correct? Use words and numbers to explain your answer.

6.  Dr. Hong prescribed 0.019 liter more medicine than Dr. Tannenbaum. Dr. Evans prescribed 0.02 less than Dr. Hong. Who prescribed the most medicine? Who prescribed the least?

**Lesson 6:**     Compare decimal fractions to the thousandths using like units, and express comparisons with >, <, =.

© 2015 Great Minds. eureka-math.org
G5-M1-TE-B1-1.3.1-1.2016

Name _____   Date _____

1. Show the numbers on the place value chart using digits. Use >, <, or = to compare. Explain your thinking in the space to the right.

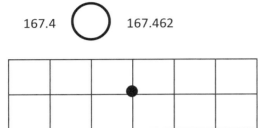

167.4 ◯ 167.462

2. Use >, <, and = to compare the numbers.

32.725 ◯ 32.735

3. Arrange the numbers in decreasing order.

76.342   76.332   76.232   76.343

_____

**Lesson 6:**  Compare decimal fractions to the thousandths using like units, and express comparisons with >, <, =.

**99**

© 2015 Great Minds. eureka-math.org
G5-M1-TE-B1-1.3.1-1.2016

Name _____     Date _____

1. Use >, <, or = to compare the following.

| | | |
|---|:---:|---|
| a.   16.45 | ◯ | 16.454 |
| b.   0.83 | ◯ | $\frac{83}{100}$ |
| c.   $\frac{205}{1000}$ | ◯ | 0.205 |
| d.   95.045 | ◯ | 95.545 |
| e.   419.10 | ◯ | 419.099 |
| f.   Five ones and eight tenths | ◯ | Fifty-eight tenths |
| g.   Thirty-six and nine thousandths | ◯ | Four tens |
| h.   One hundred four and twelve hundredths | ◯ | One hundred four and two thousandths |
| i.   One hundred fifty-eight thousandths | ◯ | 0.58 |
| j.   703.005 | ◯ | Seven hundred three and five hundredths |

2. Arrange the numbers in increasing order.

   a.   8.08    8.081    8.09    8.008

   _____

   b.   14.204    14.200    14.240    14.210

   _____

EUREKA
MATH

3. Arrange the numbers in decreasing order.

   a. 8.508  8.58  7.5  7.058

   _____

   b. 439.216  439.126  439.612  439.261

   _____

4. James measured his hand. It was 0.17 meter. Jennifer measured her hand. It was 0.165 meter. Whose hand is bigger? How do you know?

5. In a paper airplane contest, Marcel's plane travels 3.345 meters. Salvador's plane travels 3.35 meters. Jennifer's plane travels 3.3 meters. Based on the measurements, whose plane traveled the farthest distance? Whose plane traveled the shortest distance? Explain your reasoning using a place value chart.

Lesson 6:    Compare decimal fractions to the thousandths using like units, and express comparisons with >, <, =.

101

© 2015 Great Minds. eureka-math.org
G5-M1-TE-B1-1.3.1-1.2016

| 5 GRADE | **Mathematics Curriculum** |  |

Topic C

# Place Value and Rounding Decimal Fractions

## 5.NBT.4

| | | |
|---|---|---|
| **Focus Standard:** | 5.NBT.4 | Use place value understanding to round decimals to any place. |
| **Instructional Days:** | 2 | |
| **Coherence**   -Links from: | G4–M1 | Place Value, Rounding, and Algorithms for Addition and Subtraction |
|                -Links to: | G6–M2 | Arithmetic Operations Including Dividing by a Fraction |

In Topic C, students generalize their knowledge of rounding whole numbers to round decimal numbers to any place. In Grades 3 and 4, vertical number lines provided a platform for students to round whole numbers to any place. In Grade 5, vertical number lines again provide support for students to make use of patterns in the base ten system, allowing knowledge of whole-number rounding (**4.NBT.3**) to be easily applied to rounding decimal values (**5.NBT.4**). The vertical number line is used initially to find more than or less than halfway between multiples of decimal units. In these lessons, students are encouraged to reason more abstractly as they use place value understanding to approximate by using nearest multiples.

Naming those nearest multiples is an application of flexibly naming decimals using like place value units. To round 3.85 to the nearest tenth, students find the nearest multiples, 3.80 (38 tenths 0 hundredths) and 3.9 (39 tenths 0 hundredths), and then decide that 3.85 (38 tenths 5 hundredths) is exactly halfway between and, therefore, must be rounded up to 3.9.

| A Teaching Sequence Toward Mastery of Place Value and Rounding Decimal Fractions |
|---|
| **Objective 1:**   Round a given decimal to any place using place value understanding and the vertical number line. <br>             (Lessons 7–8) |

# Lesson 7

Objective:  Round a given decimal to any place using place value understanding and the vertical number line.

## Suggested Lesson Structure

■ Fluency Practice        (12 minutes)
■ Application Problem      (8 minutes)
■ Concept Development      (30 minutes)
■ Student Debrief         (10 minutes)
**Total Time**           **(60 minutes)**

**NOTES ON MULTIPLE MEANS OF REPRESENTATION:**

Vertical number lines may be a novel representation for students. Their use offers an important scaffold for students' understanding of rounding in that numbers are quite literally rounded up and down to the nearest multiple rather than left or right as in a horizontal number line. Consider showing both a horizontal and vertical line and comparing their features so that students can see the parallels and gain comfort in the use of the vertical line.

## Fluency Practice  (12 minutes)

- Sprint:  Find the Midpoint **5.NBT.4**          (7 minutes)
- Compare Decimal Fractions **5.NBT.3b**        (2 minutes)
- Rename the Units **5.NBT.2**                (3 minutes)

### Sprint:  Find the Midpoint  (7 minutes)

Materials:  (S) Find the Midpoint Sprint

Note:  Practicing this skill in isolation helps students conceptually understand the rounding of decimals.

### Compare Decimal Fractions  (2 minutes)

Materials:  (S) Personal white board

Note:  This review fluency activity helps students work toward mastery of comparing decimal numbers, a topic introduced in Lesson 6.

**NOTES ON MULTIPLE MEANS OF ENGAGEMENT:**

Fluency activities like Compare Decimal Fractions may be made more active by allowing students to stand and use their arms to make the >, <, and = signs in response to questions on the board.

    T:  (Write 12.57 ____ 12.75.) On your personal boards, compare the numbers using the greater than, less than, or equal sign.

    S:  (Write 12.57 < 12.75 on boards.)

Repeat the process and procedure:

$0.67$ ___ $\frac{67}{100}$          $\frac{83}{100}$ ___ $0.084$          $328.2$ ___ $328.099$

4.07 ___ forty-seven tenths          twenty-four and 9 thousandths ___ 3 tens

**EUREKA MATH**          Lesson 7:   Round a given decimal to any place using place value understanding          **103**
and the vertical number line.

© 2015 Great Minds. eureka-math.org
G5-M1-TE-B1-1.3.1-1.2016

### Rename the Units  (3 minutes)

Note:  Renaming decimals using various units strengthens student understanding of place value and provides an anticipatory set for rounding decimals in Lessons 7 and 8.

T:  (Write 1.5 = _____ tenths.) Fill in the blank.

S:  15 tenths.

T:  (Write 1.5 = 15 tenths. Below it, write 2.5 = _____ tenths.) Fill in the blank.

S:  25 tenths.

T:  (Write 2.5 = 25 tenths. Below it, write 12.5 = _____ tenths.) Fill in the blank.

S:  125 tenths.

Repeat the process for 17.5, 27.5, 24.5, 24.3, and 42.3.

## Application Problem  (8 minutes)

Craig, Randy, Charlie, and Sam ran in a 5K race on Saturday. They were the top 4 finishers. Here are their race times:

Craig:  25.9 minutes          Randy:  32.2 minutes

Charlie:  32.28 minutes       Sam:  25.85 minutes

Who won first place? Who won second place? Third? Fourth?

Note:  This Application Problem offers students a quick review of yesterday's concept before moving toward the rounding of decimals. Students may need reminding that in a race, the lowest number indicates the fastest time.

**Lesson 7:**      Round a given decimal to any place using place value understanding
                                      and the vertical number line.

EUREKA
MATH

## Concept Development  (30 minutes)

Materials:  (S) Personal white board, hundreds to thousandths place value chart (Template)

**Problem 1**

Strategically decompose 155 using multiple units to round to the nearest ten and nearest hundred.

T:   Work with your partner to name 155 in unit form. Next, rename 155 using the greatest number of tens possible. Finally, rename 155 using only ones. Record your ideas on your place value chart.

| Hundreds | Tens | Ones | Tenths |
|----------|------|------|--------|
| 1 | 5 | 5 | |
| | 15 | 5 | |
| | | 155 | |

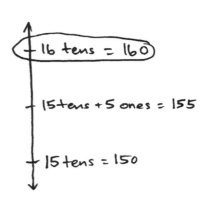

T:   Which decomposition of 155 helps you round this number to the nearest ten? Turn and talk.

S:   15 tens and 5 ones. → The one that shows 15 tens. This helps me see that 155 is between 15 tens and 16 tens on the number line. It is exactly halfway, so 155 would round to the next greater ten, which is 16 tens, or 160.

T:   Let's record that on the number line. (Record both of the nearest multiples of ten, the halfway point, and the number being rounded. Circle the correct rounded figure.)

T:   Using your chart, which of these representations helps you round 155 to the nearest 100? Turn and talk to your partner about how you will round.

S:   The one that shows 1 hundred. → I can see that 155 is between 1 hundred and 2 hundred. → The midpoint between 1 hundred and 2 hundred is 150. 155 is past the midpoint, so 155 is closer to 2 hundreds. It rounds up to 200.

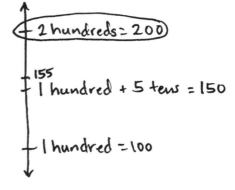

T:   Label your number line with the nearest multiples of one hundred, the halfway point, and the number we're rounding. Then, circle the one to which 155 would round.

Lesson 7:   Round a given decimal to any place using place value understanding and the vertical number line.

**Problem 2**

Strategically decompose 1.57 to round to the nearest whole and nearest tenth.

T:   Work with your partner to name 1.57 in unit form. Next,
     rename 1.57 using the greatest number of tenths possible.
     Finally, rename 1.57 using only hundredths. Record your ideas
     on your place value chart.

S:   (Work and share.)

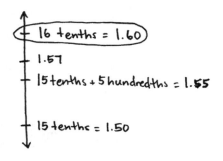

| Ones | Tenths | Hundredths |
|------|--------|------------|
| 1    | 5      | 7          |
|      | 15     | 7          |
|      |        | 157        |

T:   Which decomposition of 1.57 best helps you to round this number to the nearest tenth? Turn and
     talk. Label your number line, and circle your rounded number.

S:   (Share.)

Bring to students' attention that this problem parallels conversions between meters and centimeters since
different units are being used to name the same quantity: 1.57 meters = 157 centimeters.

**Problem 3**

Strategically decompose to round 4.381 to the nearest ten, one, tenth, and hundredth.

T:   Work with your partner to decompose 4.381 using as many tens, ones, tenths, and hundredths as
     possible. Record your work on your place value chart.

S:   (Share.)

| Tens | Ones | Tenths | Hundredths | Thousandths |
|------|------|--------|------------|-------------|
| 0    | 4    | 3      | 8          | 1           |
|      |      | 43     | 8          | 1           |
|      |      |        | 438        | 1           |
|      |      |        |            | 4381        |

T:   We want to round this number to the nearest ten first. How many tens did you
     need to name this number?

S:   Zero tens.

T:   Between what two multiples of 10 will we place this number on the number
     line? Turn and talk. Draw your number line, and circle your rounded number.

S:   (Share.)

T:   Work with your partner to round 4.381 to the nearest one, tenth, and
     hundredth. Explain your thinking with a number line.

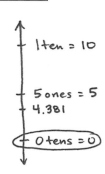

Follow the sequence from above to guide students in realizing that the number 4.381
rounds down to 4 ones, up to 44 tenths (4.4), and down to 438 hundredths (4.38).

---

**Problem 4**

Strategically decompose to round 9.975 to the nearest one, ten, tenth, and hundredth.

| Tens | Ones | Tenths | Hundredths | Thousandths |
|------|------|--------|------------|-------------|
|      | 9    | 9      | 7          | 5           |
|      |      | 99     | 7          | 5           |
|      |      |        | 997        | 5           |
|      |      |        |            | 9975        |

Follow a sequence similar to the previous problem to lead students in rounding to the given places. This problem can prove to be a problematic rounding case. Naming the number with different units, however, allows students to choose easily between nearest multiples of the given place value.

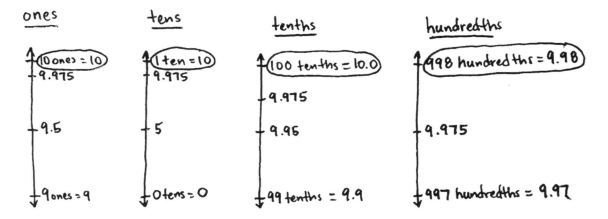

Repeat this sequence with 99.799. Round to the nearest ten, one, tenth, and hundredth.

## Problem Set  (10 minutes)

Students should do their personal best to complete the Problem Set within the allotted 10 minutes. For some classes, it may be appropriate to modify the assignment by specifying which problems they work on first. Some problems do not specify a method for solving. Students solve these problems using the RDW approach used for Application Problems.

On this Problem Set, it is suggested that all students begin with Problems 1, 2, 3, and 5 and possibly leave Problem 4 until the end if they still have time.

Before circulating while students work, review the Debrief questions relevant to the Problem Set to better guide students to a deeper understanding of, and skill with, the lesson's objective.

Lesson 7:   Round a given decimal to any place using place value understanding and the vertical number line.

107

## Student Debrief (10 minutes)

**Lesson Objective:** Round a given decimal to any place using place value understanding and the vertical number line.

The Student Debrief is intended to invite reflection and active processing of the total lesson experience.

Invite students to review their solutions for the Problem Set. They should check work by comparing answers with a partner before going over answers as a class. Look for misconceptions or misunderstandings that can be addressed in the Debrief. Guide students in a conversation to debrief the Problem Set and process the lesson.

Any combination of the questions below may be used to lead the discussion.

- In Problem 2, which decomposition helps you most if you want to round to the hundredths place? The tens place? Ones place? Why?

- How was Problem 1 different from both Problem 2 and 3? (While students may offer many differences, the salient point here is that Problem 1 is already rounded to the nearest hundredth and tenth.)

- Unit choice is the foundation of the current lesson. Problem 3 on the Problem Set offers an opportunity to discuss how the choice of unit affects the result of rounding. Be sure to allow time for these important understandings to be articulated by asking the following: If a number rounds up when rounded to the nearest tenth, does it follow that it will round up when rounded to the nearest hundredth? Thousandth? Why or why not? How do we decide about rounding up or down? How does the unit we are rounding to affect the position of the number relative to the midpoint?

- Problem 3 also offers a chance to discuss how 9-numbers often round to the same number regardless of the unit to which they are rounded. Point out that decomposing to smaller units makes this type of number easier to round. The decompositions make it simpler to identify which numbers to use as endpoints on the number line.

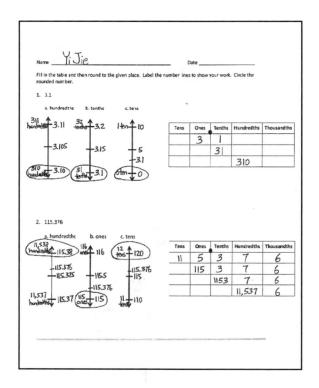

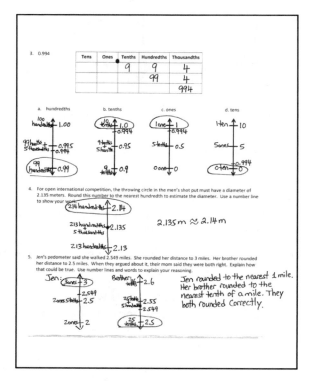

Lesson 7: Round a given decimal to any place using place value understanding and the vertical number line.

Extension: Problem 5 offers an opportunity to discuss the effect rounding to different places has on the accuracy of a measurement. Which rounded value is closest to the actual measurement? Why? In this problem, does that difference in accuracy matter? In another situation, might those differences in accuracy be more important? What should be considered when deciding to round, and to which place one might round? (For some students, this may lead to an interest in significant digits and their role in measurement in other disciplines.)

## Exit Ticket  (3 minutes)

After the Student Debrief, instruct students to complete the Exit Ticket. A review of their work will help with assessing students' understanding of the concepts that were presented in today's lesson and planning more effectively for future lessons. The questions may be read aloud to the students.

Lesson 7:     Round a given decimal to any place using place value understanding and the vertical number line.

109

© 2015 Great Minds. eureka-math.org
G5-M1-TE-B1-1.3.1-1.2016

# A

Number Correct: _____

Find the Midpoint

| | | | | | | |
|---|---|---|---|---|---|---|
| 1. | 0 | 10 | 23. | 8.5 | 8.6 |
| 2. | 0 | 1 | 24. | 2.8 | 2.9 |
| 3. | 0 | 0.01 | 25. | 0.03 | 0.04 |
| 4. | 10 | 20 | 26. | 0.13 | 0.14 |
| 5. | 1 | 2 | 27. | 0.37 | 0.38 |
| 6. | 2 | 3 | 28. | 80 | 90 |
| 7. | 3 | 4 | 29. | 90 | 100 |
| 8. | 7 | 8 | 30. | 8 | 9 |
| 9. | 1 | 2 | 31. | 9 | 10 |
| 10. | 0.1 | 0.2 | 32. | 0.8 | 0.9 |
| 11. | 0.2 | 0.3 | 33. | 0.9 | 1 |
| 12. | 0.3 | 0.4 | 34. | 0.08 | 0.09 |
| 13. | 0.7 | 0.8 | 35. | 0.09 | 0.1 |
| 14. | 0.1 | 0.2 | 36. | 26 | 27 |
| 15. | 0.01 | 0.02 | 37. | 7.8 | 7.9 |
| 16. | 0.02 | 0.03 | 38. | 1.26 | 1.27 |
| 17. | 0.03 | 0.04 | 39. | 29 | 30 |
| 18. | 0.07 | 0.08 | 40. | 9.9 | 10 |
| 19. | 6 | 7 | 41. | 7.9 | 8 |
| 20. | 16 | 17 | 42. | 1.59 | 1.6 |
| 21. | 38 | 39 | 43. | 1.79 | 1.8 |
| 22. | 0.4 | 0.5 | 44. | 3.99 | 4 |

Lesson 7: Round a given decimal to any place using place value understanding and the vertical number line.

EUREKA
MATH

# B

Number Correct: _____

Improvement: _____

Find the Midpoint

| | | | | | | |
|---|---|---|---|---|---|---|
| 1. | 10 | 20 | 23. | 0.7 | 0.8 |
| 2. | 1 | 2 | 24. | 4.7 | 4.8 |
| 3. | 0.1 | 0.2 | 25. | 2.3 | 2.4 |
| 4. | 0.01 | 0.02 | 26. | 0.02 | 0.03 |
| 5. | 0 | 10 | 27. | 0.12 | 0.13 |
| 6. | 0 | 1 | 28. | 0.47 | 0.48 |
| 7. | 1 | 2 | 29. | 80 | 90 |
| 8. | 2 | 3 | 30. | 90 | 100 |
| 9. | 6 | 7 | 31. | 8 | 9 |
| 10. | 1 | 2 | 32. | 9 | 10 |
| 11. | 0.1 | 0.2 | 33. | 0.8 | 0.9 |
| 12. | 0.2 | 0.3 | 34. | 0.9 | 1 |
| 13. | 0.3 | 0.4 | 35. | 0.08 | 0.09 |
| 14. | 0.6 | 0.7 | 36. | 0.09 | 0.1 |
| 15. | 0.1 | 0.2 | 37. | 36 | 37 |
| 16. | 0.01 | 0.02 | 38. | 6.8 | 6.9 |
| 17. | 0.02 | 0.03 | 39. | 1.46 | 1.47 |
| 18. | 0.03 | 0.04 | 40. | 39 | 40 |
| 19. | 0.06 | 0.07 | 41. | 9.9 | 10 |
| 20. | 7 | 8 | 42. | 6.9 | 7 |
| 21. | 17 | 18 | 43. | 1.29 | 1.3 |
| 22. | 47 | 48 | 44. | 6.99 | 7 |

Lesson 7:    Round a given decimal to any place using place value understanding and the vertical number line.

111

Name _____  Date _____

Fill in the table, and then round to the given place. Label the number lines to show your work. Circle the rounded number.

1.  3.1

    a. Hundredths   b. Tenths   c. Tens

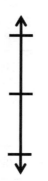 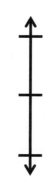 

| Tens | Ones | Tenths | Hundredths | Thousandths |
|------|------|--------|------------|-------------|
|      |      |        |            |             |
|      |      |        |            |             |
|      |      |        |            |             |

2.  115.376

    a. Hundredths   b. Ones   c. Tens

 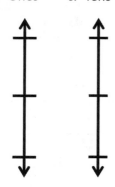

| Tens | Ones | Tenths | Hundredths | Thousandths |
|------|------|--------|------------|-------------|
|      |      |        |            |             |
|      |      |        |            |             |
|      |      |        |            |             |
|      |      |        |            |             |

**Lesson 7:**   Round a given decimal to any place using place value understanding and the vertical number line.

EUREKA MATH

3.  0.994

| Tens | Ones | Tenths | Hundredths | Thousandths |
|------|------|--------|------------|-------------|
|      |      |        |            |             |
|      |      |        |            |             |
|      |      |        |            |             |

a. Hundredths

b. Tenths

c. Ones

d. Tens

4.  For open international competition, the throwing circle in the men's shot put must have a diameter of 2.135 meters. Round this number to the nearest hundredth. Use a number line to show your work.

5.  Jen's pedometer said she walked 2.549 miles. She rounded her distance to 3 miles. Her brother rounded her distance to 2.5 miles. When they argued about it, their mom said they were both right. Explain how that could be true. Use number lines and words to explain your reasoning.

Lesson 7:    Round a given decimal to any place using place value understanding and the vertical number line.

113

Name _____ Date _____

Use the table to round the number to the given places. Label the number lines, and circle the rounded value.

8.546

| Tens | Ones | • | Tenths | Hundredths | Thousandths |
|------|------|---|--------|------------|-------------|
|      | 8    | • | 5      | 4          | 6           |
|      |      | • | 85     | 4          | 6           |
|      |      | • |        | 854        | 6           |
|      |      | • |        |            | 8546        |

a. Hundredths

b. Tens

**Lesson 7:** Round a given decimal to any place using place value understanding and the vertical number line.

EUREKA MATH

Name _____ Date _____

Fill in the table, and then round to the given place. Label the number lines to show your work. Circle the rounded number.

1.  4.3

    a. Hundredths    b. Tenths    c. Ones

| Tens | Ones | Tenths | Hundredths | Thousandths |
|------|------|--------|------------|-------------|
|      |      |        |            |             |
|      |      |        |            |             |
|      |      |        |            |             |

2.  225.286

    a. Hundredths    b. Ones    c. Tens

| Tens | Ones | Tenths | Hundredths | Thousandths |
|------|------|--------|------------|-------------|
|      |      |        |            |             |
|      |      |        |            |             |
|      |      |        |            |             |
|      |      |        |            |             |

**EUREKA MATH**®

**Lesson 7:**  Round a given decimal to any place using place value understanding and the vertical number line.

**115**

© 2015 Great Minds. eureka-math.org
G5-M1-TE-B1-1.3.1-1.2016

3.  8.984

| Tens | Ones | Tenths | Hundredths | Thousandths |
|------|------|--------|------------|-------------|
|      |      |        |            |             |
|      |      |        |            |             |
|      |      |        |            |             |
|      |      |        |            |             |

   a. Hundredths          b. Tenths              c. Ones                d. Tens

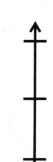     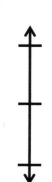     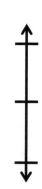

4.  On a Major League Baseball diamond, the distance from the pitcher's mound to home plate is 18.386 meters.

   a.  Round this number to the nearest hundredth of a meter. Use a number line to show your work.


   b.  How many centimeters is it from the pitcher's mound to home plate?


5.  Jules reads that 1 pint is equivalent to 0.473 liters. He asks his teacher how many liters there are in a pint. His teacher responds that there are about 0.47 liters in a pint. He asks his parents, and they say there are about 0.5 liters in a pint. Jules says they are both correct. How can that be true? Explain your answer.

Lesson 7:    Round a given decimal to any place using place value understanding and the vertical number line.

© 2015 Great Minds. eureka-math.org
G5-M1-TE-B1-1.3.1-1.2016

EUREKA MATH

| Thousandths | | | | | |
|---|---|---|---|---|---|
| **Hundredths** | | | | | |
| **Tenths** | | | | | |
| **•** | | | | | |
| **Ones** | | | | | |
| **Tens** | | | | | |
| **Hundreds** | | | | | |

hundreds to thousandths place value chart

© 2015 Great Minds. eureka-math.org
G5-M1-TE-B1-1.3.1-1.2016

# Lesson 8

Objective:  Round a given decimal to any place using place value understanding and the vertical number line.

## Suggested Lesson Structure

■ Fluency Practice          (12 minutes)
■ Application Problem       (6 minutes)
□ Concept Development       (32 minutes)
■ Student Debrief          (10 minutes)

**Total Time**             **(60 minutes)**

## Fluency Practice  (12 minutes)

- Rename the Units  **5.NBT.3**          (6 minutes)
- Round to Different Place Values  **5.NBT.4**     (6 minutes)

### Rename the Units  (6 minutes)

Note:  Decomposing common units as decimals strengthens student understanding of place value.

> T:  (Write 13 tenths = ____ .) Say the decimal.
> S:  One and 3 tenths.

Repeat the process for 14 tenths, 24 tenths, 124 tenths, and 524 tenths.

> T:  Name the number of tenths. (Write 2.5.)
> S:  25 tenths.

Repeat the process for 17.5, 27.5, 24.5, 24.3, and 42.3. Then, repeat the entire process, but with hundredths.

> T:  (Write 37 hundredths = ____ .) Say the decimal.
> S:  0.37.
> T:  (Write 37 hundredths = 0.37. Below it, write 137 hundredths = ____ .) Say the decimal.
> S:  1.37.

Repeat the process for 537 hundredths and 296 hundredths.

> T:  (Write 0.548 = ____ thousandths.) Say the number sentence.
> S:  0.548 = 548 thousandths.

Lesson 8:     Round a given decimal to any place using place value understanding and the vertical number line.

**EUREKA MATH**

T:  (Write 0.548 = 548 thousandths. Below it, write 1.548 = _____ thousandths.) Say the number sentence.

S:  1.548 = 1548 thousandths.

Repeat the process for 2.548 and 7.352.

## Round to Different Place Values  (6 minutes)

Materials:  (S) Personal white board

Note:  Reviewing this skill introduced in Lesson 7 helps students work toward mastery of rounding decimal numbers to different place values.

Although the approximation sign (≈) is used in Grade 4, a quick review of its meaning may be in order.

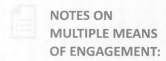

**NOTES ON MULTIPLE MEANS OF ENGAGEMENT:**

*Turn and talk* is a strategy intended to broaden active student participation by offering opportunity for all to speak during a lesson. Spend time in the beginning of the school year helping students understand what turn and talk looks like and sounds like by demonstrating with a student for the whole class. Modeling knee-to-knee, eye-to-eye body posture and active listening expectations (e.g., restating one's partner's ideas in one's own words) make for successful implementation of this powerful strategy.

T:  (Project 8.735.) Say the number.

S:  8 and 735 thousandths.

T:  Draw a vertical number line on your boards with two endpoints and a midpoint.

T:  Between what two ones is 8.735?

S:  8 ones and 9 ones.

T:  What's the midpoint for 8 and 9?

S:  8.5.

T:  Fill in your endpoints and midpoint.

T:  8.5 is the same as how many tenths?

S:  85 tenths.

T:  How many tenths are in 8.735?

S:  87 tenths.

T:  Is 87 tenths more than or less than 85 tenths?

S:  More than.

T:  (Write 8.735 ≈ _____.) Show 8.735 on your number line. Write the number sentence, when rounded to the nearest one.

S:  (Write 8.735 between 8.5 and 9 on the number line and write 8.735 ≈ 9.)

Repeat the process for the tenths place and hundredths place. Follow the same process and procedure for 7.458.

**Lesson 8:**   Round a given decimal to any place using place value understanding and the vertical number line.

119

## Application Problem (6 minutes)

Organic whole wheat flour sells in bags weighing 2.915 kilograms.

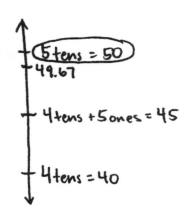

a. How much flour is this when rounded to the nearest tenth? Use a place value chart and number line to explain your thinking.

b. How much flour is this when rounded to the nearest one?

Extension: What is the difference of the two answers?

Note: This problem is a review of yesterday's lesson on rounding. The extension serves as an opportunity for students to recall the work they did in Grade 4 when subtracting fractions.

## Concept Development (32 minutes)

Materials: (S) Personal white board, hundreds to thousandths place value chart (Lesson 7 Template)

**Problem 1**

Round 49.67 to the nearest ten.

T: Turn and talk to your partner about the different ways 49.67 could be decomposed. On your place value chart, show the decomposition that you think will be most helpful in rounding to the nearest ten.

| Tens | Ones | Tenths | Hundredths |
|------|------|--------|------------|
| 4 | 9 | 6 | 7 |
|  | 49 | 6 | 7 |
|  |  | 496 | 7 |

T: Which one of these decompositions did you decide was the most helpful?

S: The decomposition with more tens is most helpful because it helps me identify the two rounding choices: 4 tens or 5 tens.

T: Draw and label a number line, and circle the rounded value. Explain your reasoning to your neighbor.

Repeat this sequence with rounding 49.67 to the nearest one and then to the nearest tenth.

Lesson 8:     Round a given decimal to any place using place value understanding and the vertical number line.

© 2015 Great Minds. eureka-math.org
G5-M1-TE-B1-1.3.1-1.2016

EUREKA MATH

**Problem 2**

Decompose 9.949 and round to the nearest tenth and hundredth. Show your work on a number line.

| Ones | Tenths | Hundredths | Thousandths |
|------|--------|-----------|-------------|
| 9    | 9      | 4         | 9           |
|      | 99     | 4         | 9           |
|      |        | 994       | 9           |

T:    What decomposition of 9.949 best helps to round this number to the nearest tenth?

S:    The one using the most tenths to name the decimal fraction. I knew I would round to either 99 tenths or 100 tenths. I looked at the hundredths. Four hundredths is not past the midpoint, so I rounded to 99 tenths. Ninety-nine tenths is the same as 9.9.

T:    Which digit made no difference when you rounded to the nearest tenth? Explain your thinking.

S:    The thousandths, because the hundredths decided which direction to round. Since there are not 5 hundredths, I rounded to the lesser number.

Repeat the process, rounding to the nearest hundredth.

**Problem 3**

A decimal number has 1 digit to the right of the decimal point. If we round this number to the nearest whole number, the result is 27. What are the maximum and minimum possible values of these two numbers? Use a number line to show your reasoning. Include the midpoint on the number line.

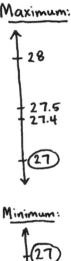

T:    (Draw a vertical number line with 3 points.)

T:    What do we know about the unknown number?

S:    It has a digit in the tenths place but nothing else beyond the tenths place. → We know that it has been rounded to 27.

T:    (Write 27 at the bottom point on the number line and circle it.) Why did I place 27 as the lesser rounded value?

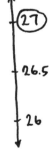

S:    We are looking for the largest number that will round down to 27. That number will be greater than 27 but less than the midpoint between 27 and 28.

T:    What is the midpoint between 27 and 28?

S:    27.5.

T:    (Place 27.5 on the number line.)

T:    If we look at numbers that have exactly 1 digit to the right of the decimal point, what is the greatest one that will round down to 27?

S:    27.4. If we go to 27.5, that would round up to 28.

Repeat the same process to find the minimum value.

EUREKA MATH

Lesson 8:    Round a given decimal to any place using place value understanding and the vertical number line.

121

© 2015 Great Minds. eureka-math.org
G5-M1-TE-B1-1.3.1-1.2016

Encourage further discussion with the following:

What if our number had exactly 2 digits to the right of the decimal point? Could I find a number larger than 27.4 that would still round down to 27? (Various answers could be expected: 27.41, 27.49, etc.). What is the largest possible value it could have? (27.49.)

A similar discussion can take place in finding the minimum when students discover that 26.5 rounds up to 27. Lead students to discover that something different happens here. Is there a number less than 26.5 with exactly 2 digits to the right of the decimal point that would still round up? (No, nothing less than 26.50.)

## Problem Set  (10 minutes)

Students should do their personal best to complete the Problem Set within the allotted 10 minutes. For some classes, it may be appropriate to modify the assignment by specifying which problems they work on first. Some problems do not specify a method for solving. Students solve these problems using the RDW approach used for Application Problems.

On this Problem Set, it is suggested that all students begin with Problems 1 and 3 and possibly leave Problem 2 until the end, if they still have time.

Before circulating while students work, review the Debrief questions relevant to the Problem Set to better guide students to a deeper understanding of a skill with the lesson's objective.

## Student Debrief  (10 minutes)

**Lesson Objective:**  Round a given decimal to any place using place value understanding and the vertical number line.

The Student Debrief is intended to invite reflection and active processing of the total lesson experience.

Invite students to review their solutions for the Problem Set. They should check work by comparing answers with a partner before going over answers as a class. Look for misconceptions or misunderstandings that can be addressed in the Debrief. Guide students in a conversation to debrief the Problem Set and process the lesson.

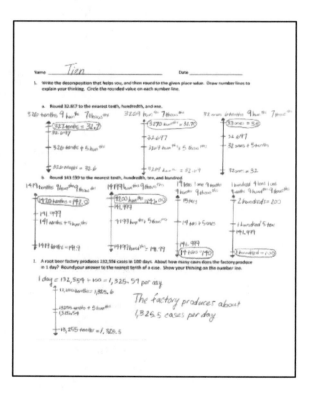

**Lesson 8:**          Round a given decimal to any place using place value understanding
                                   and the vertical number line.

**EUREKA MATH**

Any combination of the questions below may be used to lead the discussion.

- Compare our approach to rounding in today's lesson and in Lesson 7. How are they alike? How are they different? (Students will likely offer many accurate responses. Lead the discussion, however, toward the notion of only choosing specific decompositions to round in today's lesson as opposed to naming every decomposition in Lesson 7. Explore which units, or place values, are worthy of attention and which are not when rounding to a specific place value. Are there patterns to these choices?)

- Once a number rounds up at one place value, does it follow then that every place value will round up? Why or why not? (Encourage students to reference their Problem Sets as evidence of their reasoning. Problem 1(b) provides an example of differing unit choices resulting in differences in rounding up and down.)

- How does the place value chart help organize your thinking when rounding?

- Finding the maximum and minimum values poses a significant increase in cognitive load and an opportunity to build excitement! Make time to deeply discuss ways of reasoning about these tasks, as they are sure to be many and varied. Consider a discussion of Problem 3 that mirrors the one in the lesson. What if our number has exactly 3 digits to the right of the decimal? Can we find a value larger than 13.74 that would round down to 13.7? (13.749.) What about 4 places or 5 places to the right of the decimal? (13.7499, 13.74999.) Encourage students to generalize that we can get infinitely close to 13.5 with a decimal that has an infinite number of nines, yet that decimal will still round down to 13.7. We can find points on the number line as close as we like, and yet they will not be equal to 13.75. Follow the discussion with the discovery that this is not true for our minimum value. There is nothing less than 13.750 that will round up to 13.8. Math journals offer a venue for students to continue to explore maximum and minimum tasks beyond today's lesson.

## Exit Ticket  (3 minutes)

After the Student Debrief, instruct students to complete the Exit Ticket. A review of their work will help with assessing students' understanding of the concepts that were presented in today's lesson and planning more effectively for future lessons. The questions may be read aloud to the students.

Lesson 8:    Round a given decimal to any place using place value understanding and the vertical number line.

© 2015 Great Minds. eureka-math.org
G5-M1-TE-B1-1.3.1-1.2016                                                                                123

Name _____ Date _____

1. Write the decomposition that helps you, and then round to the given place value. Draw number lines to explain your thinking. Circle the rounded value on each number line.

   a. Round 32.697 to the nearest tenth, hundredth, and one.

   b. Round 141.999 to the nearest tenth, hundredth, ten, and hundred.

2. A root beer factory produces 132,554 cases in 100 days. About how many cases does the factory produce in 1 day? Round your answer to the nearest tenth of a case. Show your thinking on the number line.

Lesson 8:     Round a given decimal to any place using place value understanding and the vertical number line.

© 2015 Great Minds. eureka-math.org
G5-M1-TE-B1-1.3.1-1.2016

3. A decimal number has two digits to the right of its decimal point. If we round it to the nearest tenth, the result is 13.7.

   a. What is the maximum possible value of this number? Use words and the number line to explain your reasoning. Include the midpoint on your number line.

   13.8

   13.7

   b. What is the minimum possible value of this decimal? Use words and the number line to explain your reasoning. Include the midpoint on your number line.

Lesson 8: Round a given decimal to any place using place value understanding and the vertical number line.

Name _____     Date _____

Round the quantity to the given place value. Draw number lines to explain your thinking. Circle the rounded value on the number line.

    a.   13.989 to the nearest tenth

    b.   382.993 to nearest hundredth

EUREKA
MATH®

Name _____ Date _____

1. Write the decomposition that helps you, and then round to the given place value. Draw number lines to explain your thinking. Circle the rounded value on each number line.

    a. 43.586 to the nearest tenth, hundredth, and one.

    b. 243.875 to nearest tenth, hundredth, ten, and hundred.

2. A trip from New York City to Seattle is 2,852.1 miles. A family wants to make the drive in 10 days, driving the same number of miles each day. About how many miles will they drive each day? Round your answer to the nearest tenth of a mile.

Lesson 8: Round a given decimal to any place using place value understanding and the vertical number line.

127

© 2015 Great Minds. eureka-math.org
G5-M1-TE-B1-1.3.1-1.2016

3.  A decimal number has two digits to the right of its decimal point. If we round it to the nearest tenth, the result is 18.6.

a.  What is the maximum possible value of this number? Use words and the number line to explain your reasoning. Include the midpoint on your number line.

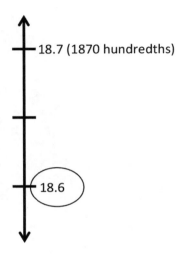

18.7 (1870 hundredths)

18.6

b.  What is the minimum possible value of this decimal? Use words, pictures, or numbers to explain your reasoning.

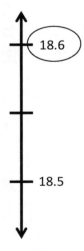

18.6

18.5

Lesson 8:     Round a given decimal to any place using place value understanding and the vertical number line.

© 2015 Great Minds. eureka-math.org
G5-M1-TE-B1-1.3.1-1.2016

EUREKA
MATH

Name _____    Date _____

1. Compare using >, <, or =.

   a.              0.4        0.127

   b.    2 thousandths + 4 hundredths        0.036

   c.    2 tens 3 tenths 1 thousandth        20.31

   d.              24 tenths        2.5

   e.    $4 \times 10^3 + 2 \times 100 + 3 \times \frac{1}{10}$        $4 \times 1000 + 2 \times 10^2 + 3 \times \frac{1}{10}$

   f.    $3 \times \frac{1}{10} + 4 \times \frac{1}{1000}$    ◯    0.340

2. Model the number 8.88 on the place value chart.

   a. Use words, numbers, and your model to explain why each of the digits has a different value. Be sure to use "ten times as large" and "one tenth as large" in your explanation.

EUREKA
MATH®

Module 1:    Place Value and Decimal Fractions

© 2015 Great Minds. eureka-math.org
G5-M1-TE-B1-1.3.1-1.2016

129

b. Multiply $8.88 \times 10^4$. Explain the shift of the digits and the change in the value of each digit.

c. Divide the product from (b) by $10^2$. Explain the shift of the digits and the change in the value of each digit.

3. Rainfall collected in a rain gauge was found to be 2.3 cm when rounded to the nearest tenth of a centimeter.

   a. Circle all the measurements below that could be the actual measurement of the rainfall.

        2.251 cm            2.349 cm            2.352 cm            2.295 cm

   b. Convert the rounded measurement to meters. Write an equation to show your work.

**EUREKA
MATH**

4.   Average annual rainfall totals for cities in New York are listed below.

| | |
|---|---|
| Rochester | 0.97 meters |
| Ithaca | 0.947 meters |
| Saratoga Springs | 1.5 meters |
| New York City | 1.268 meters |

a.   Put the rainfall measurements in order from least to greatest. Write the smallest total rainfall in word form and expanded form.

b.   Round each of the rainfall totals to the nearest tenth.

c.   Imagine New York City's rainfall is the same every year. How much rain would fall in 100 years?

d.   Write an equation using an exponent that would express the 100-year total rainfall. Explain how the digits have shifted position and why.

| Mid-Module Assessment Task | Topics A–C |
| Standards Addressed | |

**Generalize place value understanding for multi-digit whole numbers**

**5.NBT.1**  Recognize that in a multi-digit number, a digit in one place represents 10 times as much as it represents in the place to its right and 1/10 of what it represents in the place to its left.

**5.NBT.2**  Explain patterns in the number of zeros of the product when multiplying a number by powers of 10, and explain patterns in the placement of the decimal point when a decimal is multiplied or divided by a power of 10. Use whole-number exponents to denote powers of 10.

**5.NBT.3**  Read, write, and compare decimals to thousandths.

   a.  Read and write decimals to thousandths using base-ten numerals, number names, and expanded form, e.g., $347.392 = 3 \times 100 + 4 \times 10 + 7 \times 1 + 3 \times (1/10) + 9 \times (1/100) + 2 \times (1/1000)$.

   b.  Compare two decimals to thousandths based on meanings of the digits in each place, using >, =, and < symbols to record the results of comparisons.

**5.NBT.4**  Use place value understanding to round decimals to any place.

**5.MD.1**  Convert among different-sized standard measurement units within a given measurement system (e.g., convert 5 cm to 0.05 m), and use these conversions in solving multi-step, real world problems.

## Evaluating Student Learning Outcomes

A Progression Toward Mastery is provided to describe steps that illuminate the gradually increasing understandings that students develop on their way to proficiency. In this chart, this progress is presented from left (Step 1) to right (Step 4). The learning goal for students is to achieve Step 4 mastery. These steps are meant to help teachers and students identify and celebrate what the students CAN do now and what they need to work on next.

| A Progression Toward Mastery | | | | |
| --- | --- | --- | --- | --- |
| Assessment Task Item and Standards Assessed | STEP 1 Little evidence of reasoning without a correct answer. (1 Point) | STEP 2 Evidence of some reasoning without a correct answer. (2 Points) | STEP 3 Evidence of some reasoning with a correct answer or evidence of solid reasoning with an incorrect answer. (3 Points) | STEP 4 Evidence of solid reasoning with a correct answer. (4 Points) |
| 1 5.NBT.3a 5.NBT.3b | Student answers none or one part correctly. | Student answers two or three parts correctly. | Student answers four or five parts correctly. | Student correctly answers all six parts: a.  >      d.  < b.  >      e.  = c.  <      f.  < |
| 2 5.NBT.1 5.NBT.2 | Student answers none or one part correctly. | Student answers two parts correctly. | Student is able to answers all parts correctly but is unable to explain his strategy in Part (a), (b), or (c) or answers three of the four parts correctly. | Student accurately models 8.88 on the place value chart and correctly: <br>■ Uses words, numbers, and a model to explain why each digit has a different value. <br>■ Finds the product of 88,800 and explains. <br>■ Finds the quotient of 888 and explains. |
| 3 5.NBT.4 5.MD.1 | Student is unable to identify any answers for Part (a) or answer Part (b) correctly. | Student identifies one or two answers correctly for Part (a) and makes an attempt to convert, but gets an incorrect solution for Part (b). | Student identifies two answers correctly for Part (a) and converts correctly for Part (b). OR Student identifies three answers correctly for Part (a) and converts with a small error for Part (b). | Student identifies all three answers correctly for Part (a) and answers Part (b) correctly: <br>a.  2.251 cm, 2.349 cm, 2.295 cm. <br>b.  $2.3 \div 10^2 = 0.023$ |

© 2015 Great Minds. eureka-math.org
G5-M1-TE-B1-1.3.1-1.2016

## A Progression Toward Mastery

| 4<br><br>5.NBT.1<br>5.NBT.2<br>5.NBT.3<br>5.NBT.4 | Student answers none or one part correctly. | Student answers two problems correctly. | Student is able to answer all parts correctly but is unable to explain the strategy in Part (d).<br>OR<br>Student answers three of the four problems correctly. | Student correctly responds:<br>a.  0.947 m, 0.97 m, 1.268 m, 1.5 m.<br>  ▪ Nine hundred forty-seven thousandths meters.<br>  ▪ $0.9 + 0.04 + 0.007$ or $(9 \times 0.1) + (4 \times 0.01) + (7 \times 0.001)$.<br>b.  Rochester ≈ 1.0 m, Ithaca ≈ 0.9 m, Saratoga Springs ≈ 1.5 m, NYC ≈ 1.3 m.<br>c.  126.8 m.<br>d.  $1.268 \times 10^2 = 126.8$, with valid explanation. |
| --- | --- | --- | --- | --- |

EUREKA MATH

Name _Zenin_____    Date _____

1.  Compare using >, <, or =.

    a.                    0.4          0.127

    b.  2 thousandths + 4 hundredths    0.036

    c.  2 tens 3 tenths 1 thousandth    20.31

    d.              24 tenths          2.5

    e.  $4 \times 10^3 + 2 \times 100 + 3 \times \frac{1}{10}$    $4 \times 1000 + 2 \times 10^2 + 3 \times \frac{1}{10}$

    f.  $3 \times \frac{1}{10} + 4 \times \frac{1}{1000}$    0.340

2.  Model the number 8.88 on the place value chart.

    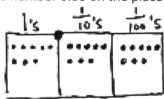

    a.  Use words, numbers, and your model to explain why each of the digits has a different value. Be sure to use "ten times as large" and "one tenth as large" in your explanation.

    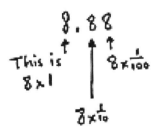

    Even though there are 8 disks in each column, they are different units so they have different values.
    8 ones is 10 times as large as 8 tenths.
    8 hundredths is $\frac{1}{10}$ as large as 8 tenths.

b. Multiply $8.88 \times 10^4$. Explain the shift of the digits and the change in the value of each digit.

$$8.88 \times 10^4 = 88,800$$

When multiplying by $10^4$, each digit shifts 4 places to the left. $10^4$ equals $10 \times 10 \times 10 \times 10$, or $10,000$, so each digit becomes $10,000$ times as large.

c. Divide the product from (b) by $10^2$. Explain the shift of the digits and the change in the value of each digit.

$$88,800 \div 10^2 = 888$$

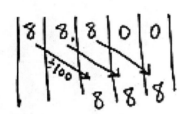

When dividing by $10^2$, each digit shifts 2 places to the right. $10^2$ equals $10 \times 10$, or $100$, so each digit becomes $\frac{1}{100}$ as large.

3. Rainfall collected in a rain gauge was found to be 2.3 cm when rounded to the nearest tenth of a centimeter.

a. Circle all the measurements below that could be the actual measurement of the rainfall.

 2.251 cm      2.349 cm      2.352 cm       2.295 cm

b. Convert the rounded measurement to meters. Write an equation to show your work.

$$2.3 \div 10^2 = 0.023$$

$$2.3 \text{ cm} = 0.023 \text{ m}$$

**EUREKA MATH**

4. Annual rainfall total for cities in New York are listed below.

| | |
|---|---|
| Rochester | 0.97 meters |
| Ithaca | 0.947 meters |
| Saratoga Springs | 1.5 meters |
| New York City | 1.268 meters |

a. Put the rainfall measurements in order from least to greatest. Write the smallest total rainfall in word form and expanded form.

$$0.947 \, m \, , \, 0.97 \, m \, , \, 1.268 \, m \, , \, 1.5 \, m$$

nine hundred forty-seven thousandths

$$9 \times \tfrac{1}{10} + 4 \times \tfrac{1}{100} + 7 \times \tfrac{1}{1000}$$

b. Round each of the rainfall totals to the nearest tenth.

$$0.97 \, m \approx 1.0 \, m$$
$$0.947 \, m \approx 0.9 \, m$$
$$1.5 \, m \approx 1.5 \, m$$
$$1.268 \, m \approx 1.3 \, m$$

c. Imagine New York City's rainfall is the same every year. How much rain would fall in 100 years?

$$1.268 \, m \times 100 = 126.8 \, m$$

126.8 m would fall in 100 years.

d. Write an equation using an exponent that would express the 100-year total rainfall. Explain how the digits have shifted position and why.

$$1.268 \, m \times 10^2 = 126.8 \, m$$

Each digit shifts 2 places to the left when multiplying by $10^2$. The value of each digit becomes 100 times as large.

$$1 \times 100 = 100$$
$$0.2 \times 100 = 20$$
$$0.06 \times 100 = 6$$
$$0.008 \times 100 = 0.8$$

Topic D

# Adding and Subtracting Decimals

## 5.NBT.2, 5.NBT.3, 5.NBT.7

| Focus Standards: | 5.NBT.2 | Explain patterns in the number of zeros of the product when multiplying a number by powers of 10, and explain patterns in the placement of the decimal point when a decimal is multiplied or divided by a power of 10. Use whole-number exponents to denote powers of 10. |
|---|---|---|
| | 5.NBT.3 | Read, write, and compare decimals to thousandths. <br> a. Read and write decimals to thousandths using base-ten numerals, number names, and expanded form, e.g., 347.392 = 3 × 100 + 4 × 10 + 7 × 1 + 3 × (1/10) + 9 × (1/100) + 2 × (1/1000). <br> b. Compare two decimals to thousandths based on meanings of the digits in each place, using >, =, and < symbols to record the results of comparisons. |
| | 5.NBT.7 | Add, subtract, multiply, and divide decimals to hundredths, using concrete models or drawings and strategies based on place value, properties of operations, and/or the relationship between addition and subtraction; relate the strategy to a written method and explain the reasoning used. |
| Instructional Days: | 2 | |
| Coherence | -Links from: | G4–M1 | Place Value, Rounding, and Algorithms for Addition and Subtraction |
| | -Links to: | G6–M2 | Arithmetic Operations Including Dividing by a Fraction |

Topics D through F mark a shift from the opening topics of Module 1. From this point to the conclusion of the module, students begin to use base ten understanding of adjacent units and whole-number algorithms to reason about and perform decimal fraction operations—addition and subtraction in Topic D, multiplication in Topic E, and division in Topic F (**5.NBT.7**).

In Topic D, unit form provides the connection that allows students to use what they know about general methods for addition and subtraction with whole numbers to reason about decimal addition and subtraction (e.g., 7 tens + 8 tens = 15 tens = 150 is analogous to 7 tenths + 8 tenths = 15 tenths = 1.5). Place value charts and disks (both concrete and pictorial representations) and the relationship between addition and subtraction are used to provide a bridge for relating such understandings to a written method. Real-world contexts provide opportunities for students to apply their knowledge of decimal addition and subtraction as well in Topic D.

| A Teaching Sequence Toward Mastery of Adding and Subtracting Decimals |
|---|
| **Objective 1:**   Add decimals using place value strategies, and relate those strategies to a written method. (Lesson 9) |
| **Objective 2:**   Subtract decimals using place value strategies, and relate those strategies to a written method. (Lesson 10) |

# Lesson 9

Objective: Add decimals using place value strategies, and relate those strategies to a written method.

## Suggested Lesson Structure

■ Fluency Practice            (14 minutes)
■ Application Problem          (5 minutes)
■ Concept Development         (31 minutes)
■ Student Debrief             (10 minutes)
   **Total Time**             **(60 minutes)**

## Fluency Practice  (14 minutes)

- Sprint:  Round to the Nearest One  **5.NBT.4**          (8 minutes)
- Decompose the Unit  **5.NBT.1**                         (2 minutes)
- Round to Different Place Values  **5.NBT.4**            (2 minutes)
- One Unit More  **5.NBT.7**                              (2 minutes)

### Sprint:  Round to the Nearest One  (8 minutes)

Materials:    (S) Round to the Nearest One Sprint

Note:  This Sprint helps students build mastery of rounding to the nearest whole number.

### Decompose the Unit  (2 minutes)

Materials:    (S) Personal white board

Note:  Decomposing common units as decimals strengthens student understanding of place value.

    T:    (Project 6.358.) Say the number.
    S:    6 and 358 thousandths.
    T:    How many tenths are in 6.358?
    S:    63 tenths.
    T:    (Write 6.358 = 63 tenths _____ thousandths.) On your boards, write the number separating the tenths.
    S:    (Write 6.358 = 63 tenths 58 thousandths.)

Repeat the process for hundredths. Follow the same process for 7.354.

---

Lesson 9:          Add decimals using place value strategies, and relate those strategies
                                             to a written method.

## Round to Different Place Values  (2 minutes)

Materials:    (S) Personal white board

Note:  Reviewing this skill introduced in Lesson 8 helps students work toward mastery of rounding decimal numbers to different place values.

- T:  (Project 2.475.) Say the number.
- S:  2 and 475 thousandths.
- T:  On your board, round the number to the nearest tenth.
- S:  (Write 2.475 ≈ 2.5.)

Repeat the process, rounding 2.457 to the nearest hundredth. Follow the same process for 2.987, but vary the sequence.

## One Unit More  (2 minutes)

Materials:    (S) Personal white board

Note:  This anticipatory fluency drill lays a foundation for the concept taught in this lesson.

- T:  (Write 5 tenths.) Say the decimal that's one-tenth more than the given value.
- S:  Six-tenths.

Repeat the process for 5 hundredths, 5 thousandths, 8 hundredths, 3 tenths, and 2 thousandths. Specify the unit to increase by.

- T:  (Write 0.052.) On your board, write one more thousandth.
- S:  (Write 0.053.)

Repeat the process for 1 tenth more than 35 hundredths, 1 thousandth more than 35 hundredths, and 1 hundredth more than 438 thousandths.

## Application Problem  (5 minutes)

Ten baseballs weigh 1,417.4 grams. About how much does 1 baseball weigh? Round your answer to the nearest tenth of a gram. Round your answer to the nearest gram. Which answer would you give if someone asked, "About how much does a baseball weigh?" Explain your choice.

Note:  The Application Problem requires students to divide by powers of ten and round. These are skills learned in the first part of this module.

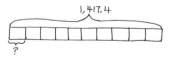

1,417.4 ÷ 10 = 141.74
Nearest tenth: 141.7
Nearest gram: 142

I'd say that a baseball weighs about 142g. Grams are small measurements, so to the nearest gram is close enough.

Lesson 9:    Add decimals using place value strategies, and relate those strategies
                   to a written method.                                    **141**

© 2015 Great Minds. eureka-math.org
G5-M1-TE-B1-1.3.1-1.2016

## Concept Development  (31 minutes)

Materials:    (S) Hundreds to thousandths place value chart (Lesson 7 Template), personal white board

**Problems 1–3**

2 tenths + 6 tenths

2 ones 3 thousandths + 6 ones 1 thousandth

2 tenths 5 thousandths + 6 hundredths

> T:   (Write 2 tenths + 6 tenths on the board.) Solve 2 tenths plus 6 tenths using disks on your place value chart.
>
> S:   (Solve.)
>
> T:   Say the sentence using unit form.
>
> S:   2 tenths + 6 tenths = 8 tenths.
>
> T:   How is this addition problem the same as a whole-number addition problem? Turn and share with your partner.
>
> S:   In order to find the sum, I added like units—tenths with tenths. → 2 tenths plus 6 tenths equals 8 tenths, just like 2 apples plus 6 apples equals 8 apples. → Since the sum is 8 tenths, we don't need to bundle or regroup.
>
> T:   (On the board, write Problems 2 and 3.) Work with your partner, and solve the next two problems with place value disks on your place value chart.

> **NOTES ON**
> **MULTIPLE MEANS**
> **OF REPRESENTATION:**
>
> Understanding the meaning of *tenths,* *hundredths,* and *thousandths* is essential. Proportional manipulatives, such as base ten blocks, can be used to ensure understanding of the vocabulary. Students should eventually move to concrete place value disks or drawing, which are more efficient.

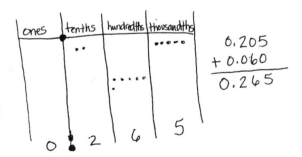

> S:   (Solve.)
>
> T:   Let's record our last problem vertically. (Write 0.205 and the plus sign underneath on the board.) What do I need to think about when I write my second addend?

Lead students to see that the vertical written method mirrors the placement of disks on the chart. Like units should be aligned with like units. Avoid procedural language like *line up the decimals.* Students should justify alignment of digits based on place value units.

© 2015 Great Minds. eureka-math.org
G5-M1-TE-B1-1.3.1-1.2016

**Problems 4–6**

1.8 + 13 tenths

1 hundred 8 hundredths + 2 ones 4 hundredths

148 thousandths + 7 ones 13 thousandths

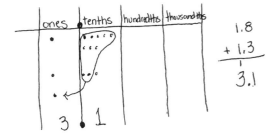

- T: (Write 1.8 + 13 tenths on the board.) Use your place value chart and draw disks to show the addends of our next problem.
- S: (Show.)
- T: Tell how you represented these addends.

Some students may represent 13 tenths by drawing 13 disks in the tenths column or as 1 disk in the ones column and 3 disks in the tenths column. Others may represent 1.8 using mixed units or only tenths.

- S: (Share.)
- T: Which way of composing these addends requires the fewest number of disks? Why?
- S: Using ones and tenths because each ones disk is worth 10 tenths disks.
- T: Will your choice of units on your place value chart affect your answer (sum)?
- S: No! Either is OK. It will still give the same answer.
- T: Add. Share your thinking with your partner.
- S: 1.8 + 13 tenths = 1 one and 21 tenths. There are 10 tenths in one whole. I can compose 2 wholes and 11 tenths from 21 tenths, so the answer is 3 and 1 tenth. → 13 tenths is the same as 1 one 3 tenths. 1 one 3 tenths + 1 one 8 tenths = 2 ones 11 tenths, which is the same as 3 ones 1 tenth.
- T: Let's record what we did on our charts. (Lead students to articulate the need to align like units in the vertical algorithm.)
- T: What do you notice that was different about this problem? What was the same? Turn and talk.
- S: We needed to rename in this problem because 8 tenths and 3 tenths is 11 tenths. → We added ones with ones and tenths with tenths—like units, just like before.
- T: (On the board, write Problems 5 and 6.) Work with your partner to solve the next two problems on your place value chart, and record your thinking vertically.
- T: (As students work 148 thousandths + 7 ones 13 thousandths, discuss which composition of 148 thousandths is the most efficient.)

**NOTES ON MULTIPLE MEANS OF ACTION AND EXPRESSION:**

Some students may struggle when asked to turn and talk to another student because they need more time to compose their thoughts. Math journals can be used in conjunction with Turn and Talk as journals provide a venue in which students can use a combination of graphics, symbols, and words to help them communicate their thinking.

## Problems 7–9

0.74 + 0.59

7.048 + 5.196

7.44 + 0.774

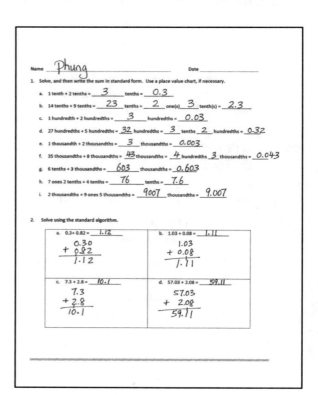

T: (Write 0.74 + 0.59 horizontally on the board.) Using disks and the place value chart, find the sum of 0.74 and 0.59. Record your work.

S: (Solve.)

T: How was this problem like others we've solved? How was it different?

S: We still add by combining like units—ones with ones, tenths with tenths, hundredths with hundredths—but this time we had to bundle in two place value units. We still record our thinking the same way we do with whole numbers—aligning like units.

T: Solve the next two problems using the written method. You may also use your disks to help you. (Write 7.048 + 5.196 and 7.44 + 0.774 on the board horizontally.)

S: (Solve.)

T: How is 7.44 + 0.704 different from the other problems we've solved? Turn and talk.

S: One addend had hundredths, and the other had thousandths. We still had to add like units. → We could think of 44 hundredths as 440 thousandths. → One addend did not have a zero in the ones place. I could leave it like that or include the zero. The missing zero did not change the quantity.

## Problem Set  (10 minutes)

Students should do their personal best to complete the Problem Set within the allotted 10 minutes. For some classes, it may be appropriate to modify the assignment by specifying which problems they work on first. Some problems do not specify a method for solving. Students solve these problems using the RDW approach used for Application Problems.

On this Problem Set, we suggest all students work directly through all problems. Please note that Problem 4 includes the word *pedometer,* which may need explanation for some students.

144

Lesson 9: Add decimals using place value strategies, and relate those strategies to a written method.

EUREKA MATH

© 2015 Great Minds. eureka-math.org
G5-M1-TE-B1-1.3.1-1.2016

## Student Debrief  (10 minutes)

**Lesson Objective:**  Add decimals using place value strategies, and relate those strategies to a written method.

The Student Debrief is intended to invite reflection and active processing of the total lesson experience.

Invite students to review their solutions for the Problem Set. They should check work by comparing answers with a partner before going over answers as a class. Look for misconceptions or misunderstandings that can be addressed in the Debrief. Guide students in a conversation to debrief the Problem Set and process the lesson.

Any combination of the questions below may be used to lead the discussion.

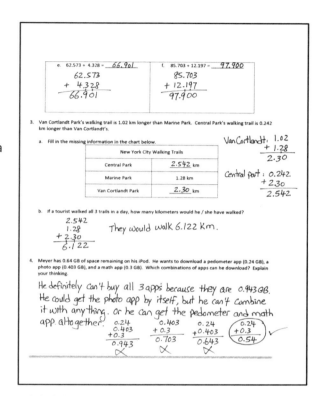

- How is adding decimal fractions the same as adding whole numbers? How is it different?

- What are some different words you have used through the grades for changing 10 smaller units for 1 of the next larger units or changing 1 unit for 10 of the next smaller units?

- What do you notice about the addends in Problems 1(b), (d), and (f)? Explain the thought process in solving these problems.

- Did you recognize a pattern in the digits used in Problem 2? Look at each row and column.

- What do you notice about the sum in Problem 2(f)? What are some different ways to express the sum? (Encourage students to name the sum using thousandths, hundredths, and tenths.) How is this problem different from adding whole numbers?

- Ask early finishers to generate addition problems that have 2 decimal place values, but add up to specific sums like 1 or 2 (e.g., 0.74 + 0.26).

## Exit Ticket  (3 minutes)

After the Student Debrief, instruct students to complete the Exit Ticket. A review of their work will help with assessing students' understanding of the concepts that were presented in today's lesson and planning more effectively for future lessons. The questions may be read aloud to the students.

Lesson 9:   Add decimals using place value strategies, and relate those strategies to a written method.

145

© 2015 Great Minds. eureka-math.org
G5-M1-TE-B1-1.3.1-1.2016

# A

**Number Correct:** _____

Round to the Nearest One

| | | |
|---|---|---|
| 1. | 3.1 ≈ | |
| 2. | 3.2 ≈ | |
| 3. | 3.3 ≈ | |
| 4. | 3.4 ≈ | |
| 5. | 3.5 ≈ | |
| 6. | 3.6 ≈ | |
| 7. | 3.9 ≈ | |
| 8. | 13.9 ≈ | |
| 9. | 13.1 ≈ | |
| 10. | 13.5 ≈ | |
| 11. | 7.5 ≈ | |
| 12. | 8.5 ≈ | |
| 13. | 9.5 ≈ | |
| 14. | 19.5 ≈ | |
| 15. | 29.5 ≈ | |
| 16. | 89.5 ≈ | |
| 17. | 2.4 ≈ | |
| 18. | 2.41 = | |
| 19. | 2.42 ≈ | |
| 20. | 2.45 ≈ | |
| 21. | 2.49 ≈ | |
| 22. | 2.51 ≈ | |

| | | |
|---|---|---|
| 23. | 12.51 ≈ | |
| 24. | 16.61 ≈ | |
| 25. | 17.41 ≈ | |
| 26. | 11.51 ≈ | |
| 27. | 11.49 ≈ | |
| 28. | 13.49 ≈ | |
| 29. | 13.51 ≈ | |
| 30. | 15.51 ≈ | |
| 31. | 15.49 ≈ | |
| 32. | 6.3 ≈ | |
| 33. | 7.6 ≈ | |
| 34. | 49.5 ≈ | |
| 35. | 3.45 ≈ | |
| 36. | 17.46 ≈ | |
| 37. | 11.76 ≈ | |
| 38. | 5.2 ≈ | |
| 39. | 12.8 ≈ | |
| 40. | 59.5 ≈ | |
| 41. | 5.45 ≈ | |
| 42. | 19.47 ≈ | |
| 43. | 19.87 ≈ | |
| 44. | 69.51 ≈ | |

Lesson 9:    Add decimals using place value strategies, and relate those strategies
to a written method.

# B

Number Correct: _____

Improvement: _____

Round to the Nearest One

| | | | | | | |
|---|---|---|---|---|---|---|
| 1. | 4.1 ≈ | | 23. | 13.51 ≈ | |
| 2. | 4.2 ≈ | | 24. | 17.61 ≈ | |
| 3. | 4.3 ≈ | | 25. | 18.41 ≈ | |
| 4. | 4.4 ≈ | | 26. | 12.51 ≈ | |
| 5. | 4.5 ≈ | | 27. | 12.49 ≈ | |
| 6. | 4.6 ≈ | | 28. | 14.49 ≈ | |
| 7. | 4.9 ≈ | | 29. | 14.51 ≈ | |
| 8. | 14.9 ≈ | | 30. | 16.51 ≈ | |
| 9. | 14.1 ≈ | | 31. | 16.49 ≈ | |
| 10. | 14.5 ≈ | | 32. | 7.3 ≈ | |
| 11. | 7.5 ≈ | | 33. | 8.6 ≈ | |
| 12. | 8.5 ≈ | | 34. | 39.5 ≈ | |
| 13. | 9.5 ≈ | | 35. | 4.45 ≈ | |
| 14. | 19.5 ≈ | | 36. | 18.46 ≈ | |
| 15. | 29.5 ≈ | | 37. | 12.76 ≈ | |
| 16. | 79.5 ≈ | | 38. | 6.2 ≈ | |
| 17. | 3.4 ≈ | | 39. | 13.8 ≈ | |
| 18. | 3.41 ≈ | | 40. | 49.5 ≈ | |
| 19. | 3.42 ≈ | | 41. | 6.45 ≈ | |
| 20. | 3.45 ≈ | | 42. | 19.48 ≈ | |
| 21. | 3.49 ≈ | | 43. | 19.78 ≈ | |
| 22. | 3.51 ≈ | | 44. | 59.51 ≈ | |

**Lesson 9:** Add decimals using place value strategies, and relate those strategies to a written method.

147

© 2015 Great Minds. eureka-math.org
G5-M1-TE-B1-1.3.1-1.2016

Name _____    Date _____

1.  Solve, and then write the sum in standard form. Use a place value chart if necessary.

    a.  1 tenth + 2 tenths = _____ tenths = _____

    b.  14 tenths + 9 tenths = _____ tenths = _____ one(s) _____ tenth(s) = _____

    c.  1 hundredth + 2 hundredths = _____ hundredths = _____

    d.  27 hundredths + 5 hundredths = _____ hundredths = _____ tenths _____ hundredths = _____

    e.  1 thousandth + 2 thousandths = _____ thousandths = _____

    f.  35 thousandths + 8 thousandths = _____ thousandths = _____ hundredths _____ thousandths = _____

    g.  6 tenths + 3 thousandths = _____ thousandths = _____

    h.  7 ones 2 tenths + 4 tenths = _____ tenths = _____

    i.  2 thousandths + 9 ones 5 thousandths = _____ thousandths = _____

2.  Solve using the standard algorithm.

    | | |
    |---|---|
    | a.   0.3 + 0.82 = _____ | b.   1.03 + 0.08 = _____ |
    | c.   7.3 + 2.8 = _____ | d.   57.03 + 2.08 = _____ |

**Lesson 9:**    Add decimals using place value strategies, and relate those strategies
to a written method.

© 2015 Great Minds. eureka-math.org
G5-M1-TE-B1-1.3.1-1.2016

**EUREKA
MATH**

| e. 62.573 + 4.328 = _____ | f. 85.703 + 12.197 = _____ |
| --- | --- |
| | |

3. Van Cortlandt Park's walking trail is 1.02 km longer than Marine Park's. Central Park's walking trail is 0.242 km longer than Van Cortlandt's.

   a. Fill in the missing information in the chart below.

| New York City Walking Trails | |
| --- | --- |
| Central Park | _____ km |
| Marine Park | 1.28 km |
| Van Cortlandt Park | _____ km |

   b. If a tourist walked all 3 trails in a day, how many kilometers would he or she have walked?

4. Meyer has 0.64 GB of space remaining on his iPod. He wants to download a pedometer app (0.24 GB), a photo app (0.403 GB), and a math app (0.3 GB). Which combinations of apps can he download? Explain your thinking.

Lesson 9: Add decimals using place value strategies, and relate those strategies to a written method.

149

Name _____ Date _____

1. Solve.

    a.   4 hundredths + 8 hundredths = _____ hundredths = _____ tenth(s) _____ hundredths

    b.   64 hundredths + 8 hundredths = _____ hundredths = _____ tenths _____ hundredths

2. Solve using the standard algorithm.

    | a.   2.40 + 1.8 = _____ | b.   36.25 + 8.67 = _____ |
    |---|---|
    | | |

**Lesson 9:**     Add decimals using place value strategies, and relate those strategies to a written method.

© 2015 Great Minds. eureka-math.org
G5-M1-TE-B1-1.3.1-1.2016

**EUREKA MATH**

Name _____ Date _____

1. Solve.

    a. 3 tenths + 4 tenths = _____ tenths

    b. 12 tenths + 9 tenths = _____ tenths = _____ one(s) _____ tenth(s)

    c. 3 hundredths + 4 hundredths = _____ hundredths

    d. 27 hundredths + 7 hundredths = _____ hundredths = _____ tenths _____ hundredths

    e. 4 thousandths + 3 thousandths = _____ thousandths

    f. 39 thousandths + 5 thousandths = _____ thousandths = _____ hundredths _____ thousandths

    g. 5 tenths + 7 thousandths = _____ thousandths

    h. 4 ones 4 tenths + 4 tenths = _____ tenths

    i. 8 thousandths + 6 ones 8 thousandths = _____ thousandths

2. Solve using the standard algorithm.

| | |
|---|---|
| a.  0.4 + 0.7 = _____ | b.  2.04 + 0.07 = _____ |
| c.  6.4 + 3.7 = _____ | d.  56.04 + 3.07 = _____ |

**EUREKA MATH**

Lesson 9:    Add decimals using place value strategies, and relate those strategies to a written method.

151

| e.   72.564 + 5.137 = _____ | f.   75.604 + 22.296 = _____ |
|---|---|
|  |  |

3.  Walkway Over the Hudson, a bridge that crosses the Hudson River in Poughkeepsie, is 2.063 kilometers long. Anping Bridge, which was built in China 850 years ago, is 2.07 kilometers long.

   a.   What is the total span of both bridges? Show your thinking.

   b.   Leah likes to walk her dog on the Walkway Over the Hudson. If she walks across and back, how far will she and her dog walk?

4.  For his parents' anniversary, Danny spends $5.87 on a photo. He also buys a balloon for $2.49 and a box of strawberries for $4.50. How much money does he spend all together?

**Lesson 9:**     Add decimals using place value strategies, and relate those strategies to a written method.

EUREKA
MATH

# Lesson 10

Objective: Subtract decimals using place value strategies, and relate those strategies to a written method.

## Suggested Lesson Structure

- ■ Fluency Practice          (10 minutes)
- ■ Application Problem        (5 minutes)
- ■ Concept Development        (35 minutes)
- ■ Student Debrief           (10 minutes)

  **Total Time**             **(60 minutes)**

## Fluency Practice  (10 minutes)

- Take Out the Unit  **5.NBT.1**          (3 minutes)
- Add Decimals  **5.NBT.7**              (3 minutes)
- One Less Unit  **5.NBT.7**             (4 minutes)

### Take Out the Unit  (3 minutes)

Materials:   (S) Personal white board

Note: Decomposing common units as decimals strengthens student understanding of place value.

- T:  (Project 76.358 = _____.) Say the number.
- S:  76 and 358 thousandths.
- T:  (Write 76.358 = 7 tens _____ thousandths.) On your personal white board, fill in the blank.
- S:  (Write 76.358 = 7 tens 6358 thousandths.)

Repeat the process for tenths and hundredths. 76.358 = 763 tenths _____ thousandths, 76.358 = _____ hundredths 8 thousandths.

### Add Decimals  (3 minutes)

Materials:   (S) Personal white board

Note: Reviewing this skill introduced in Lesson 9 helps students work toward mastery of adding common decimal units.

- T:  (Write 3 tenths + 2 tenths = _____.) Write the addition sentence in standard form.
- S:  0.3 + 0.2 = 0.5.

Repeat the process for 5 hundredths + 4 hundredths and 35 hundredths + 4 hundredths.

Lesson 10:    Subtract decimals using place value strategies, and relate those
              strategies to a written method.

153

## One Unit Less  (4 minutes)

Materials:    (S) Personal white board

Note:  This anticipatory fluency drill lays a foundation for the concept taught in this lesson.

> T:    (Write 5 tenths.) Say the decimal that is 1 tenth less than the given unit.
> S:    0.4.

Repeat the process for 5 hundredths, 5 thousandths, 7 hundredths, and 9 tenths.

> T:    (Write 0.029.) On your board, write the decimal that is one less thousandth.
> S:    (Write 0.028.)

Repeat the process for 1 tenth less than 0.61, 1 thousandth less than 0.061, and 1 hundredth less than 0.549.

Note:  This fluency is a review of skills learned in Lesson 9.

## Application Problem  (5 minutes)

At the 2012 London Olympics, Michael Phelps won the gold medal in the men's 100-meter butterfly. He swam the first 50 meters in 26.96 seconds. The second 50 meters took him 25.39 seconds. What was his total time?

Note:  Adding decimal numbers is a skill learned in Lesson 9.

## Concept Development  (35 minutes)

Materials:    (S) Hundreds to thousandths place value chart (Lesson 7 Template), personal white board

**Problem 1**

5 tenths – 3 tenths

7 ones 5 thousandths – 2 ones 3 thousandths

9 hundreds 5 hundredths – 3 hundredths

> T:    (Write 5 tenths – 3 tenths on the board.) Let's read this expression aloud together. Turn and tell your partner how you'll solve this problem, and then find the difference using your place value chart and disks.
> T:    Explain your reasoning when solving this subtraction expression.
> S:    Since the units are alike, we can just subtract. 5 – 3 = 2. → This problem is very similar to 5 ones minus 3 ones, or 5 people minus 2 people. The units may change, but the basic fact 5 – 2 = 3 is the same.

Lesson 10:      Subtract decimals using place value strategies, and relate those
                                strategies to a written method.                                          EUREKA
                          © 2015 Great Minds. eureka-math.org                                            MATH
                          G5-M1-TE-B1-1.3.1-1.2016

T:   (Write 7 ones 5 thousandths – 2 ones 3 thousandths on the board.) Find the difference. Solve this problem with the place value chart and disks. Record your thinking vertically, using the algorithm.

S:   (Solve.)

T:   What did you have to think about as you wrote the problem vertically?

S:   Like units are being subtracted, so my work should also show that. Ones with ones and thousandths with thousandths.

T:   (Write 9 hundreds 5 hundredths – 3 hundredths on board.) Solve 9 hundreds 5 hundredths – 3 hundredths. Read carefully, and then tell your neighbor how you'll solve this problem.

S:   In word form, these units look similar, but they're not. I'll just subtract 3 hundredths from 5 hundredths.

T:   Use your place value chart to help you solve, and record your thinking vertically.

NOTES ON
MULTIPLE MEANS
OF ENGAGEMENT:

Support oral or written responses with sentence frames, such as _____ is _____ hundredths. Allow the use of place value charts and the sentence frames to scaffold the process of converting units in subtraction. Some students need concrete materials to support their learning, as renaming in various units may not yet be an abstract construct for them.

## Problems 2–3

83 tenths – 6.4

9.2 – 6 ones 4 tenths

T:   (Write 83 tenths – 6.4 = _____ on the board.) How is this problem different from the problems we've seen previously?

S:   This problem involves regrouping.

S:   (Solve using disks, recording their work in the standard algorithm.)

T:   Share how you solved.

S:   We had to regroup before we could subtract tenths from tenths. Then, we subtracted ones from ones using the same process as with whole numbers.

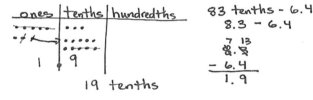

Repeat the sequence with 9.2 – 6 ones 4 tenths. Students may use various strategies to solve. Comparison of strategies makes for interesting discussion.

EUREKA
MATH

Lesson 10:     Subtract decimals using place value strategies, and relate those strategies to a written method.

155

© 2015 Great Minds. eureka-math.org
G5-M1-TE-B1-1.3.1-1.2016

**Problems 4–5**

0.831 – 0.292

4.083 – 1.29

6 – 0.48

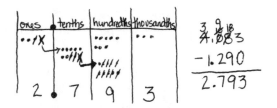

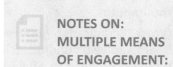

T:   (Write 0.831 - 0.292 on the board.) Use your disks to solve. Record your work vertically using the standard algorithm.

S:   (Write and share.)

T:   (Write 4.083 – 1.29 on the board.) What do you notice about the thousandths place? Turn and talk.

S:   There is no digit in the thousandths place in 1.29. → We can think of 29 hundredths as 290 thousandths. In this case, I don't have to change units because there are no thousandths that must be subtracted.

T:   Solve with your disks and record.

> **NOTES ON:**
> **MULTIPLE MEANS**
> **OF ENGAGEMENT:**
>
> Students may be more engaged with the concept of adding and subtracting decimal fractions when reminded that these are the same skills needed for managing money.

Repeat the sequence with 6 – 0.48. While some students may use a mental strategy to find the difference, others will use disks to regroup in order to subtract. Continue to stress the alignment based on like units when recording vertically. When the ones place is aligned, students will recognize that there are not as many digits in the minuend of 6 wholes as in the subtrahend of 48 hundredths. Ask, "How can we think about 6 wholes in the same units as 48 hundredths?" Then, lead students to articulate the need to record 6 ones as 600 hundredths or 6.00 in order to subtract vertically. Ask, "By decomposing 6 wholes into 600 hundredths, have we changed its value?" (No, we just converted it to smaller units—similar to exchanging six dollars for 600 pennies.)

## Problem Set  (10 minutes)

Students should do their personal best to complete the Problem Set within the allotted 10 minutes. For some classes, it may be appropriate to modify the assignment by specifying which problems they work on first. Some problems do not specify a method for solving. Students solve these problems using the RDW approach used for Application Problems.

With this Problem Set, it is suggested that students begin with Problems 1–4 and possibly leave Problem 5 until the end, if they still have time. Alternatively, be selective about which items from Problems 2 and 3 are required. This lends time for all to complete Problem 5.

© 2015 Great Minds. eureka-math.org
G5-M1-TE-B1-1.3.1-1.2016

EUREKA
MATH

## Student Debrief (10 minutes)

**Lesson Objective:** Subtract decimals using place value strategies, and relate those strategies to a written method.

The Student Debrief is intended to invite reflection and active processing of the total lesson experience.

Invite students to review their solutions for the Problem Set. They should check work by comparing answers with a partner before going over answers as a class. Look for misconceptions or misunderstandings that can be addressed in the Debrief. Guide students in a conversation to debrief the Problem Set and process the lesson.

Any combination of the questions below may be used to lead the discussion.

- How is subtracting decimal fractions the same as subtracting whole numbers? How is it different?

- Look at Problem 2(a), (b), and (c). What process did you use to find the difference in each of these problems?

- Did you have to use the standard algorithm to solve each of the problems in Problem 3? Look at Problem 3(b) and (c). Which was more challenging? Why?

- In Problem 3(f), how did you think about finding the difference between 59 hundredths and 2 ones 4 tenths? Explain your approach.

- How could you change Mrs. Fan's question in Problem 4 so that Michael's answer is correct?

- Take time during the Debrief to explore any miscues in Problem 5 with the phrase *less than*.

## Exit Ticket (3 minutes)

After the Student Debrief, instruct students to complete the Exit Ticket. A review of their work will help with assessing students' understanding of the concepts that were presented in today's lesson and planning more effectively for future lessons. The questions may be read aloud to the students.

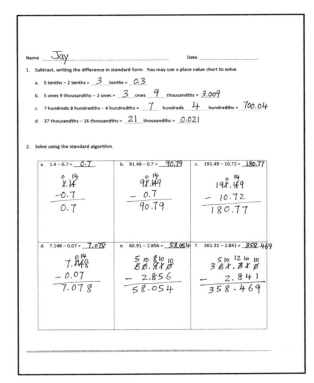

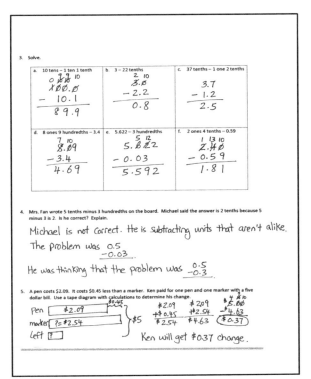

Name _____ Date _____

1. Subtract, writing the difference in standard form. You may use a place value chart to solve.

   a.  5 tenths – 2 tenths = _____ tenths = _____

   b.  5 ones 9 thousandths – 2 ones = _____ ones _____ thousandths = _____

   c.  7 hundreds 8 hundredths – 4 hundredths = _____ hundreds _____ hundredths = _____

   d.  37 thousandths – 16 thousandths = _____ thousandths = _____

2. Solve using the standard algorithm.

| a.  1.4 – 0.7 = _____ | b.  91.49 – 0.7 = _____ | c.  191.49 – 10.72 = _____ |
|---|---|---|
| d.  7.148 – 0.07 = _____ | e.  60.91 – 2.856 = _____ | f.  361.31 – 2.841 = _____ |

Lesson 10:  Subtract decimals using place value strategies, and relate those strategies to a written method.

© 2015 Great Minds. eureka-math.org
G5-M1-TE-B1-1.3.1-1.2016

EUREKA MATH

3. Solve.

| | | |
|---|---|---|
| a. 10 tens – 1 ten 1 tenth | b. 3 – 22 tenths | c. 37 tenths – 1 one 2 tenths |
| d. 8 ones 9 hundredths – 3.4 | e. 5.622 – 3 hundredths | f. 2 ones 4 tenths – 0.59 |

4. Mrs. Fan wrote *5 tenths minus 3 hundredths* on the board. Michael said the answer is 2 tenths because 5 minus 3 is 2. Is he correct? Explain.

5. A pen costs $2.09. It costs $0.45 less than a marker. Ken paid for one pen and one marker with a five-dollar bill. Use a tape diagram with calculations to determine his change.

Lesson 10: Subtract decimals using place value strategies, and relate those strategies to a written method.

© 2015 Great Minds. eureka-math.org
G5-M1-TE-B1-1.3.1-1.2016

Name _____ Date _____

1. Subtract.

    1.7 – 0.8 = _____ tenths – _____ tenths = _____ tenths = _____

2. Subtract vertically, showing all work.

    a.   84.637 – 28.56 = _____

    b.   7 – 0.35 = _____

Lesson 10:   Subtract decimals using place value strategies, and relate those strategies to a written method.

© 2015 Great Minds. eureka-math.org
G5-M1-TE-B1-1.3.1-1.2016

EUREKA MATH

Name _____ Date _____

1. Subtract. You may use a place value chart.

   a. 9 tenths – 3 tenths = _____ tenths

   b. 9 ones 2 thousandths – 3 ones = _____ ones _____ thousandths

   c. 4 hundreds 6 hundredths – 3 hundredths = _____ hundreds _____ hundredths

   d. 56 thousandths – 23 thousandths = _____ thousandths = _____ hundredths _____ thousandths

2. Solve using the standard algorithm.

| | | |
|---|---|---|
| a. 1.8 – 0.9 = _____ | b. 41.84 – 0.9 = _____ | c. 341.84 – 21.92 = _____ |
| d. 5.182 – 0.09 = _____ | e. 50.416 – 4.25 = _____ | f. 741 – 3.91 = _____ |

Lesson 10: Subtract decimals using place value strategies, and relate those strategies to a written method.

161

© 2015 Great Minds. eureka-math.org
G5-M1-TE-B1-1.3.1-1.2016

3. Solve.

| | | |
|---|---|---|
| a. 30 tens − 3 tens 3 tenths | b. 5 − 16 tenths | c. 24 tenths − 1 one 3 tenths |
| d. 6 ones 7 hundredths − 2.3 | e. 8.246 − 5 hundredths | f. 5 ones 3 tenths − 0.53 |

4. Mr. House wrote *8 tenths minus 5 hundredths* on the board. Maggie said the answer is 3 hundredths because 8 minus 5 is 3. Is she correct? Explain.

5. A clipboard costs $2.23. It costs $0.58 more than a notebook. Lisa bought two clipboards and one notebook. She paid with a ten-dollar bill. How much change does Lisa get? Use a tape diagram to show your thinking.

Lesson 10: Subtract decimals using place value strategies, and relate those strategies to a written method.

# Mathematics Curriculum

## Topic E
# Multiplying Decimals

**5.NBT.2, 5.NBT.3, 5.NBT.7**

| Focus Standards: | 5.NBT.2 | Explain patterns in the number of zeros of the product when multiplying a number by powers of 10, and explain patterns in the placement of the decimal point when a decimal is multiplied or divided by a power of 10. Use whole-number exponents to denote powers of 10. |
|---|---|---|
| | 5.NBT.3 | Read, write, and compare decimals to thousandths. |
| | | a. Read and write decimals to thousandths using base-ten numerals, number names, and expanded form, e.g., 347.392 = 3 × 100 + 4 × 10 + 7 × 1 + 3 × (1/10) + 9 × (1/100) + 2 × (1/1000). |
| | | b. Compare two decimals to thousandths based on meanings of the digits in each place, using >, =, and < symbols to record the results of comparisons. |
| | 5.NBT.7 | Add, subtract, multiply, and divide decimals to hundredths, using concrete models or drawings and strategies based on place value, properties of operations, and/or the relationship between addition and subtraction; relate the strategy to a written method and explain the reasoning used. |
| **Instructional Days:** | 2 | |
| **Coherence** -Links from: | G4–M3 | Multi-Digit Multiplication and Division |
| -Links to: | G5–M2 | Multi-Digit Whole Number and Decimal Fraction Operations |
| | G6–M2 | Arithmetic Operations Including Dividing by a Fraction |

A focus on reasoning about the multiplication of a decimal fraction by a one-digit whole number in Topic E provides the link that connects Grade 4 multiplication work and Grade 5 fluency with multi-digit multiplication. Place value understanding of whole-number multiplication coupled with an area model of the distributive property is used to help students build direct parallels between whole-number products and the products of one-digit multipliers and decimals (**5.NBT.7**). Once the decimal has been placed, students use an estimation-based strategy to confirm the reasonableness of the product through place value reasoning. Word problems provide a context within which students can reason about products.

**A Teaching Sequence Toward Mastery of Multiplying Decimals**

**Objective 1:** Multiply a decimal fraction by single-digit whole numbers, relate to a written method through application of the area model and place value understanding, and explain the reasoning used.
(Lesson 11)

**Objective 2:** Multiply a decimal fraction by single-digit whole numbers, including using estimation to confirm the placement of the decimal point.
(Lesson 12)

# Lesson 11

Objective:  Multiply a decimal fraction by single-digit whole numbers, relate to a written method through application of the area model and place value understanding, and explain the reasoning used.

## Suggested Lesson Structure

- ■ Fluency Practice          (10 minutes)
- ■ Application Problem        (5 minutes)
- ▢ Concept Development        (35 minutes)
- ■ Student Debrief           (10 minutes)

   **Total Time**              **(60 minutes)**

## Fluency Practice  (10 minutes)

- Take Out the Unit  **5.NBT.1**          (4 minutes)
- Add and Subtract Decimals  **5.NBT.7**     (6 minutes)

### Take Out the Unit  (4 minutes)

Materials:    (S) Personal white board

Note:  Decomposing common units as decimals strengthens student understanding of place value.

   T:   (Project 1.234 = _____ thousandths.) Say the number. Think about how many thousandths are in 1.234.

   T:   (Project 1.234 = 1234 thousandths.) How much is one thousand thousandths?

   S:   One thousand thousandths is the same as 1.

   T:   (Project 65.247 = _____.) Say the number in unit form.

   S:   65 ones 247 thousandths.

   T:   (Write 76.358 = 7 tens _____ thousandths.) On your personal white board, fill in the blank.

   S:   (Write 76.358 = 7 tens 6358 thousandths.)

Repeat the process for 76.358 = 763 tenths _____ thousandths and 76.358 = _____ hundredths 8 thousandths.

**Lesson 11:**    Multiply a decimal fraction by single-digit whole numbers, relate to a written method through application of the area model and place value understanding, and explain the reasoning used.

165

## Add and Subtract Decimals  (6 minutes)

Materials:    (S) Personal white board

Note:  Reviewing these skills introduced in Lessons 9 and 10 helps students work toward mastery of adding and subtracting common decimal units.

> T:    (Write 7258 thousandths + 1 thousandth = _____.) Write the addition sentence in standard form.
> S:    7.258 + 0.001 = 7.259.

Repeat the process for 7 ones 258 thousandths + 3 hundredths, 7 ones 258 thousandths + 4 tenths, 6 ones 453 thousandths + 4 hundredths, 2 ones 37 thousandths + 5 tenths, and 6 ones 35 hundredths + 7 thousandths.

> T:    (Write 4 ones 8 hundredths – 2 ones = ____ ones ____ hundredths.) Write the subtraction sentence in standard form.
> S:    (Write 4.08 – 2 = 2.08.)

Repeat the process for 9 tenths 7 thousandths – 4 thousandths, 4 ones 582 thousandths – 3 hundredths, 9 ones 708 thousandths – 4 tenths, and 4 ones 73 thousandths – 4 hundredths.

## Application Problem  (5 minutes)

After school, Marcus ran 3.2 km, and Cindy ran 1.95 km. Who ran farther? How much farther?

Note:  This Application Problem requires students to subtract decimal numbers, as studied in Lesson 10.

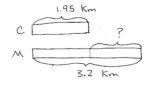

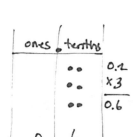

## Concept Development  (35 minutes)

Materials:    (S) Hundreds to thousandths place value chart (Lesson 7 Template), personal white board

### Problems 1–3

$3 \times 0.2 = 0.6$

$3 \times 0.3 = 0.9$

$4 \times 0.3 = 1.2$

> T:    Draw 2 tenths on your place value chart.
> S:    (Draw.)
> T:    Make 3 copies of 2 tenths. How many tenths do you have in all?
> S:    6 tenths.
> T:    With your partner, write the algorithm showing 6 tenths.
> S:    I wrote 0.2 + 0.2 + 0.2 = 0.6 because I added 2 tenths three times to get 6 tenths. → I multiplied 2 tenths by 3 and got 6 tenths. So, I wrote $3 \times 0.2 = 0.6$.

Multiply a decimal fraction by single-digit whole numbers, relate to a written method through application of the area model and place value understanding, and explain the reasoning used.

EUREKA MATH

T:  (On the board, write 3 copies of 2 tenths is _____.) Complete the sentence. Say the equation in unit form.

S:  6 tenths; 3 × 2 tenths = 6 tenths.

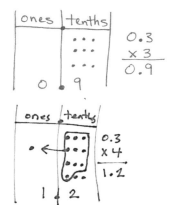

T:  Work with your partner to find the values of 3 × 0.3 and 4 × 0.3.

S:  (Work to solve.)

T:  How was 4 × 3 tenths different from 3 × 3 tenths?

S:  I had to bundle the 10 tenths. I made 1 one, and I had 2 tenths left. I didn't do this before. → We made a number greater than 1 whole.

T:  4 copies of 3 tenths is 12 tenths. (Show on the place value chart.) 12 tenths is the same as _____.

S:  1 one and 2 tenths.

**Problems 4–6**

2 × 0.43 = 0.86

2 × 0.423 = 0.846

4 × 0.423 = 1.692

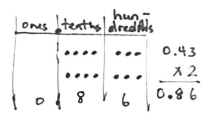

T:  (On the board, write 2 × 0.43 = _____.) How can we use our knowledge from the previous problems to solve this problem?

S:  We can make copies of hundredths like we made copies of tenths. → A hundredth is a different unit, but we can multiply it just like a tenth.

T:  Use your place value chart to find the product of 2 × 0.43. Complete the sentence, "2 copies of 43 hundredths is _____."

S:  (Work.)

T:  Read what your place value chart shows.

S:  I have 2 groups of 4 tenths and 2 groups of 3 hundredths. I need to combine tenths with tenths and hundredths with hundredths.

T:  (Draw an area model.) Let me record what I hear you saying. Discuss with your partner the difference between these two models.

**NOTES ON MULTIPLE MEANS OF ACTION AND EXPRESSION:**

The area model can be considered a graphic organizer. It organizes the partial products. Some students may need support in order to remember which product goes in each cell of the area model, especially as the model becomes more complex. The organizer can be modified by writing the expressions in each cell. This might eliminate the need for some students to visually track the product into the appropriate cell.

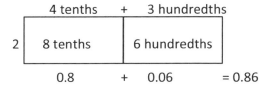

S:  (Share observations.)

**Lesson 11:**   Multiply a decimal fraction by single-digit whole numbers, relate to a written method through application of the area model and place value understanding, and explain the reasoning used.                    **167**

© 2015 Great Minds. eureka-math.org
G5-M1-TE-B1-1.3.1-1.2016

T:   (On the board, write 2 × 0.423 = _____.)
     What is different about this problem?

S:   There is a digit in the thousandths place.
     → We are multiplying thousandths.

T:   Use your place value chart to solve this
     problem. (Allow students time to work.)

T:   Read what your place value chart
     shows.

S:   846 thousandths.

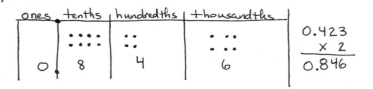

T:   Now, draw an area model, and write an
     equation with the partial products to
     show how you found the product. (Allow
     students time to draw.)

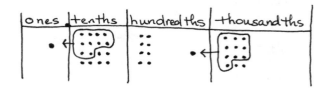

| 4 tenths | + 2 hundredths | + 3 thousandths |
|---|---|---|
| 8 tenths | 4 hundredths | 6 thousandths |
| 0.8 | + 0.04 | + 0.006  = 0.846 |

(2 is to the left of this table)

T:   (Write 4 × 0.423 = _____ on the board.)
     Solve by drawing on your place value chart.

S:   (Solve.)

T:   Read the number that is shown on your
     chart.

S:   1 and 692 thousandths.

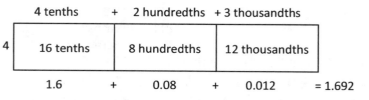

T:   How was this problem different from the
     last?

S:   4 times 3 thousandths is 12 thousandths,
     so we had to bundle 10 thousandths to
     make 1 hundredth.

| 4 tenths | + 2 hundredths | + 3 thousandths |
|---|---|---|
| 16 tenths | 8 hundredths | 12 thousandths |
| 1.6 | + 0.08 | + 0.012  = 1.692 |

(4 is to the left of this table)

T:   Did any other units have to be regrouped?

S:   The units in the tenths place. Four times 4 tenths is
     16 tenths, so we had to regroup 10 tenths to make
     1 whole.

T:   Let's record what happened using an area model and
     an equation showing the partial products.

**Problems 7–9**

Use the area model to represent the distributive property.

6 × 1.21

7 × 2.41

8 × 2.34

T:   (On the board, write 6 × 1.21 = _____.) Let's
     imagine our disks but use an area model to represent
     our thinking as we find the product of 6 times 1 and
     21 hundredths.

**NOTES ON
MULTIPLE MEANS
OF ENGAGEMENT:**

It can be highly motivating for students
to recognize their progress. Teachers
can help students do this by creating
a list of skills and concepts students
will master in this module. Students can
keep track as the module and their
skills progress.

**Lesson 11:**      Multiply a decimal fraction by single-digit whole numbers, relate to a
                      written method through application of the area model and place value
                      understanding, and explain the reasoning used.

                      © 2015 Great Minds. eureka-math.org
                      G5-M1-TE-B1-1.3.1-1.2016

**EUREKA
MATH**

T:  (On the board, draw a rectangle for the area model.) On our area model, how many sections do we have?

S:  3. We have one for each place.

T:  (Divide the rectangle into three sections and label the area model.) I have a section for 1 whole, 2 tenths, and 1 hundredth. I am multiplying each by what number?

S:  6.

T:  With a partner, solve the equation using an area model and an equation that shows the partial products.

S:  (Work with partners to solve.)

Have students solve the last two expressions using area models and recording equations. Circulate. Look for any misconceptions.

## Problem Set  (10 minutes)

Students should do their personal best to complete the Problem Set within the allotted 10 minutes. For some classes, it may be appropriate to modify the assignment by specifying which problems they work on first. Some problems do not specify a method for solving. Students solve these problems using the RDW approach used for Application Problems.

## Student Debrief  (10 minutes)

**Lesson Objective:** Multiply a decimal fraction by single-digit whole numbers, relate to a written method through application of the area model and place value understanding, and explain the reasoning used.

The Student Debrief is intended to invite reflection and active processing of the total lesson experience.

Invite students to review their solutions for the Problem Set. They should check work by comparing answers with a partner before going over answers as a class. Look for misconceptions or misunderstandings that can be addressed in the Debrief. Guide students in a conversation to debrief the Problem Set and process the lesson.

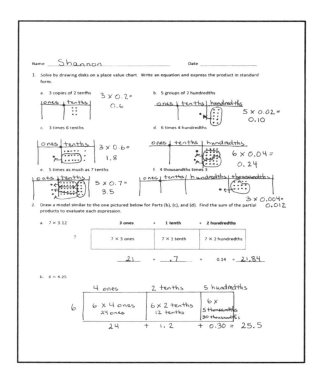

Lesson 11:    Multiply a decimal fraction by single-digit whole numbers, relate to a written method through application of the area model and place value understanding, and explain the reasoning used.

169

Any combination of the questions below may be used to lead the discussion.

- Compare student work in Problems 1(c) and 1(d), as some students may regroup units while others may not. Give an opportunity for students to discuss the equality of the various unit decompositions. Give other examples (e.g., 6 × 0.25), asking students to defend the equality of 1.50, 150 hundredths, and 1.5 with words, models, and numbers.

- Problem 3 points out a common error in student thinking when multiplying decimals by whole numbers. Allow students to share their models for correcting Miles's error. Students should be able to articulate which units are being multiplied and composed into larger ones.

- Problem 3 also offers an opportunity to extend understanding. Ask students to find the expression that has 14.42 as the product and 7 as the multiplicand. Ask students to show their work using an area model.

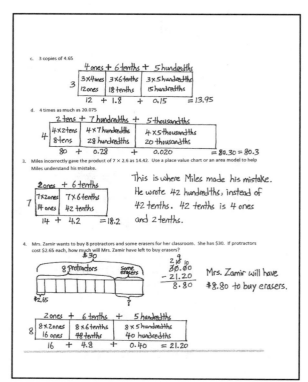

### Exit Ticket  (3 minutes)

After the Student Debrief, instruct students to complete the Exit Ticket. A review of their work will help with assessing students' understanding of the concepts that were presented in today's lesson and planning more effectively for future lessons. The questions may be read aloud to the students.

Lesson 11:    Multiply a decimal fraction by single-digit whole numbers, relate to a written method through application of the area model and place value understanding, and explain the reasoning used.

EUREKA MATH

Name _____ Date _____

1. Solve by drawing disks on a place value chart. Write an equation, and express the product in standard form.

   a. 3 copies of 2 tenths

   b. 5 groups of 2 hundredths

   c. 3 times 6 tenths

   d. 6 times 4 hundredths

   e. 5 times as much as 7 tenths

   f. 4 thousandths times 3

2. Draw a model similar to the one pictured below for Parts (b), (c), and (d). Find the sum of the partial products to evaluate each expression.

   a. $7 \times 3.12$

   | | 3 ones | + | 1 tenth | + | 2 hundredths |
   |---|---|---|---|---|---|
   | 7 | $7 \times 3$ ones | | $7 \times 1$ tenth | | $7 \times 2$ hundredths |

   _____ + _____ + 0.14 = _____

   b. $6 \times 4.25$

Lesson 11: Multiply a decimal fraction by single-digit whole numbers, relate to a written method through application of the area model and place value understanding, and explain the reasoning used.

171

EUREKA MATH

c.   3 copies of 4.65

d.   4 times as much as 20.075

3.   Miles incorrectly gave the product of $7 \times 2.6$ as 14.42. Use a place value chart or an area model to help Miles understand his mistake.

4.   Mrs. Zamir wants to buy 8 protractors and some erasers for her classroom. She has $30. If protractors cost $2.65 each, how much will Mrs. Zamir have left to buy erasers?

**Lesson 11:**   Multiply a decimal fraction by single-digit whole numbers, relate to a written method through application of the area model and place value understanding, and explain the reasoning used.

© 2015 Great Minds. eureka-math.org
G5-M1-TE-B1-1.3.1-1.2016

Name _____ Date _____

1.  Solve by drawing disks on a place value chart. Write an equation, and express the product in standard form.

    4 copies of 3 tenths

2.  Complete the area model, and then find the product.

    3 × 9.63

    _____ _____ _____ _____

    _____ | 3 × ____ ones | 3 × ____ tenths | 3 × ____ hundredths |

**Lesson 11:**   Multiply a decimal fraction by single-digit whole numbers, relate to a
written method through application of the area model and place value
understanding, and explain the reasoning used.

**173**

EUREKA MATH®

© 2015 Great Minds. eureka-math.org
G5-M1-TE-B1-1.3.1-1.2016

Name _____   Date _____

1. Solve by drawing disks on a place value chart. Write an equation, and express the product in standard form.

    a.  2 copies of 4 tenths

    b.  4 groups of 5 hundredths

    c.  4 times 7 tenths

    d.  3 times 5 hundredths

    e.  9 times as much as 7 tenths

    f.  6 thousandths times 8

2. Draw a model similar to the one pictured below. Find the sum of the partial products to evaluate each expression.

    a.  4 × 6.79

| 6 ones | + | 7 tenths | + | 9 hundredths |
|---|---|---|---|---|
| 4 × 6 ones | | 4 × 7 tenths | | 4 × 9 hundredths |

(4)

_____ + _____ + _____ = _____

Lesson 11: Multiply a decimal fraction by single-digit whole numbers, relate to a written method through application of the area model and place value understanding, and explain the reasoning used.

© 2015 Great Minds. eureka-math.org
G5-M1-TE-B1-1.3.1-1.2016

EUREKA MATH

b.  6 × 7.49

c.  9 copies of 3.65

d.  3 times 20.175

3.  Leanne multiplied 8 × 4.3 and got 32.24. Is Leanne correct? Use an area model to explain your answer.

4.  Anna buys groceries for her family. Hamburger meat is $3.38 per pound, sweet potatoes are $0.79 each, and hamburger rolls are $2.30 a bag. If Anna buys 3 pounds of meat, 5 sweet potatoes, and 1 bag of hamburger rolls, what will she pay in all for the groceries?

Lesson 11:    Multiply a decimal fraction by single-digit whole numbers, relate to a
              written method through application of the area model and place value
              understanding, and explain the reasoning used.

© 2015 Great Minds. eureka-math.org
G5-M1-TE-B1-1.3.1-1.2016

175

# Lesson 12

Objective:  Multiply a decimal fraction by single-digit whole numbers, including using estimation to confirm the placement of the decimal point.

## Suggested Lesson Structure

■ Fluency Practice          (12 minutes)
■ Application Problem        (8 minutes)
■ Concept Development        (30 minutes)
■ Student Debrief           (10 minutes)

   **Total Time**              **(60 minutes)**

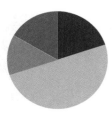

## Fluency Practice  (12 minutes)

- Sprint: Add Decimals  **5.NBT.7**      (9 minutes)
- Find the Product  **5.NBT.7**          (3 minutes)

### Sprint: Add Decimals  (9 minutes)

Materials:    (S) Add Decimals Sprint

Note:  This Sprint helps students build automaticity in adding decimals without renaming.

### Find the Product  (3 minutes)

Materials:    (S) Personal white board

Note:  Reviewing this skill introduced in Lesson 11 helps students work toward mastery of multiplying single-digit numbers times decimals.

   T:  (Write 4 × 2 ones = __.) Write the multiplication sentence.
   S:  4 × 2 = 8.
   T:  Say the multiplication sentence in unit form.
   S:  4 × 2 ones = 8 ones.

Repeat the process for 4 × 0.2, 4 × 0.02, 5 × 3, 5 × 0.3, 5 × 0.03, 3 × 0.2, 3 × 0.03, 3 × 0.23, and 2 × 0.14.

Lesson 12:    Multiply a decimal fraction by single-digit whole numbers, including using estimation to confirm the placement of the decimal point.

© 2015 Great Minds. eureka-math.org
G5-M1-TE-B1-1.3.1-1.2016

## Application Problem  (8 minutes)

Patty buys 7 juice boxes a month for lunch. If one juice box costs $2.79, how much money does Patty spend on juice each month? Use an area model to solve.

Extension:  How much will Patty spend on juice in 10 months? In 12 months?

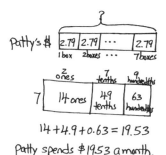

Note:  The first part of this Application Problem asks students to multiply a number with two decimal digits by a single-digit whole number. This skill, taught in Lesson 11, provides a bridge to today's topic, which involves reasoning about such problems on a more abstract level. The extension problem looks back to Topic A and requires multiplication by powers of 10. Although students have not multiplied a decimal number by a two-digit number, they can solve 12 × 2.79 by using the distributive property: (10 × 2.79) + (2 × 2.79).

## Concept Development  (30 minutes)

Materials:    (S) Personal white board

**Problems 1–3**

31 × 4 = 124

3.1 × 4 = 12.4

0.31 × 4 = 1.24

T:   (Write all three problems on the board.) How are these three problems alike?

S:   They are alike because they all have 3, 1, and 4 as part of the problem.

T:   Use an area model to find the products.

S:   (Draw.)

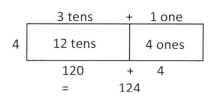

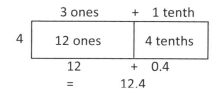

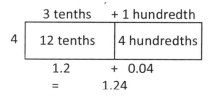

Lesson 12:    Multiply a decimal fraction by single-digit whole numbers, including          177
              using estimation to confirm the placement of the decimal point.

© 2015 Great Minds. eureka-math.org
G5-M1-TE-B1-1.3.1-1.2016

T:  How are the products of all three problems alike?

S:  Every product has the digits 1, 2, and 4, and they are always in the same order.

T:  If the products have the same digits and those digits are in the same order, do the products have the same value? Why or why not? Turn and talk.

S:  The decimal is not in the same place in every product. → No. The values are different because the units that we multiplied are different. → The digits that we multiplied are the same, but you have to think about the units to make sure the answer is right.

T:  So, let me repeat what I hear you saying. I can multiply the numerals first and then think about the units to help place the decimal.

**NOTES ON MULTIPLE MEANS OF ACTION AND EXPRESSION:**

Web-based applications like Number Navigator offer assistance to those whose fine motor skills may prevent them from being able to set out columnar arithmetic with ease. Such applications preclude the need for complicated spreadsheets, making them an ideal scaffold for the classroom.

**Problems 4–6**

$5.1 \times 6 = 30.6$

$11.4 \times 4 = 45.6$

$7.8 \times 3 = 23.4$

T:  (Write $5.1 \times 6$ on the board.) What is the smallest unit in 5.1?

S:  Tenths.

T:  Multiply 5.1 by 10 to convert it to tenths. How many tenths is the same as 5.1?

S:  51 tenths.

```
    5  1   tenths
  ×    6
  ─────────
  3 0  6   tenths
```

T:  Suppose our multiplication sentence was $51 \times 6$. Multiply and record your multiplication vertically. What is the product?

S:  306.

T:  We know that our product will contain these digits, but is 306 a reasonable product for our actual problem of $5.1 \times 6$? Turn and talk.

S:  We have to think about the units. 306 ones is not reasonable, but 306 tenths is. → 5.1 is close to 5, and $5 \times 6 = 30$, so the answer should be around 30. → 306 tenths is the same as 30 ones and 6 tenths.

T:  Using this reasoning, where does it make sense to place the decimal in 306? What is the product of $5.1 \times 6$?

S:  Between the zero and the six. The product is 30.6.

T:  (Write $11.4 \times 4 =$ _____ on the board.) What is the smallest unit in 11.4?

S:  Tenths.

T:  What power of 10 must I use to convert 11.4 to tenths? How many tenths are the same as 11 ones 4 tenths? Turn and talk.

S:  $10^1$. → We have to multiply by 10. → 11.4 is the same as 114 tenths.

Lesson 12:     Multiply a decimal fraction by single-digit whole numbers, including using estimation to confirm the placement of the decimal point.

T:  Multiply vertically to find the product of 114 tenths × 4.

S:  456 tenths.

T:  We know that our product will contain these digits. How will we
    determine where to place our decimal?

S:  We can estimate. 11.4 is close to 11, and 11 × 4 is 44. The only place
    that makes sense for the decimal is between the five and six. The actual
    product is 45.6. → 456 tenths is the same as 45 ones and 6 tenths.

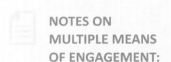

|   | 1 | 1 | 4 | tenths |
|---|---|---|---|--------|
|   | × |   | 4 |        |
|   | 4 | 5 | 6 | tenths |

Repeat the sequence with 7.8 × 3. Elicit from students the similarities and differences between this problem
and others. (Must compose tenths into ones.)

**Problems 7–9**

3.12 × 4 = 12.48

3.22 × 5 = 16.10

3.42 × 6 = 20.52

T:  (Write 3.12 × 4 on the board.) Use hundredths to
    name 3.12 and multiply vertically by 4. What is the
    product?

S:  1248 hundredths.

T:  I will write four possible products for 3.12 × 4 on my
    board. Turn and talk to your partner about which of
    these products is reasonable. Then, confirm the actual
    product using an area model. Be prepared to share
    your thinking. (Write 1248, 1.248, 12.48, and 124.8 on
    the board.)

S:  (Work and share.)

NOTES ON
MULTIPLE MEANS
OF ENGAGEMENT:

Once students are able to determine
the reasonable placement of decimals
through estimation, by composition
of smaller units to larger units, and
by using the area model, teachers
should have students articulate which
strategy they might choose first.
Students who have choices develop
self-determination and feel more
connected to their learning.

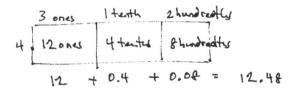

Repeat this sequence for the other problems in this set. Write possible products, and allow students to
reason about decimal placement both from an estimation-based strategy and from a composition of smaller
units into larger units (e.g., 2,052 hundredths is the same as 20 ones and 52 hundredths). Students should
also find the products using an area model and then compare the two methods for finding products.

EUREKA
MATH           Lesson 12:       Multiply a decimal fraction by single-digit whole numbers, including        179
                                using estimation to confirm the placement of the decimal point.

**Problems 10–12**

0.733 × 4 = 2.932

10.733 × 4 = 42.932

5.733 × 4 = 22.932

T:  (Write 0.733 × 4 on the board.) Rename 0.733 using its smallest units, and multiply vertically by 4. What is the product?

S:  2,932 thousandths.

T:  (Write 2.932, 29.32, 293.2, and 2,932 on the board.) Which of these is the most reasonable product for 0.733 × 4? Why? Turn and talk.

S:  2.932. 0.733 is close to one whole, and 1 × 4 = 4. None of the other choices make sense. → I know that 2,000 thousandths make 2 wholes, so 2,932 thousandths is the same as 2 ones 932 thousandths.

T:  Solve 0.733 × 4 using an area model. Compare your products using these two different strategies.

Repeat this sequence for 10.733 × 4, and allow independent work for 5.733 × 4. Require students to decompose to smallest units to reason about decimal placement and the area model so that products and strategies may be compared.

## Problem Set  (10 minutes)

Students should do their personal best to complete the Problem Set within the allotted 10 minutes. For some classes, it may be appropriate to modify the assignment by specifying which problems they work on first. Some problems do not specify a method for solving. Students solve these problems using the RDW approach used for Application Problems.

## Student Debrief  (10 minutes)

**Lesson Objective:**  Multiply a decimal fraction by single-digit whole numbers, including using estimation to confirm the placement of the decimal point.

The Student Debrief is intended to invite reflection and active processing of the total lesson experience.

Invite students to review their solutions for the Problem Set. They should check work by comparing answers with a partner before going over answers as a class. Look for misconceptions or misunderstandings that can be addressed in the Debrief. Guide students in a conversation to debrief the Problem Set and process the lesson.

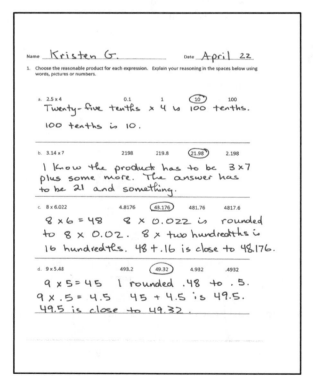

---

Lesson 12:  Multiply a decimal fraction by single-digit whole numbers, including using estimation to confirm the placement of the decimal point.

Any combination of the questions below may be used to lead the discussion.

- How can whole-number multiplication help you with decimal multiplication? (Elicit from students that the digits in a product can be found through whole-number multiplication. The actual product can be deduced through estimation-based logic or composing smaller units into larger units.)

- How does the area model help you to justify the placement of the decimal point for the product in 1(b)?

- Problem 3 offers an excellent opportunity to discuss purposes of estimation because multiple answers are possible for the estimate Marcel gives his gym teacher. For example, Marcel could round to 4 km and estimate that he bikes about 16 miles. Another way to estimate is to round each leg of the trip to 3.5 km. The estimated total distance is then 14 km. Allow time for students to defend their thoughts. It may also be fruitful to compare their thoughtful estimates with the exact answer. Which estimate is closer to the actual distance? In which cases would it matter?

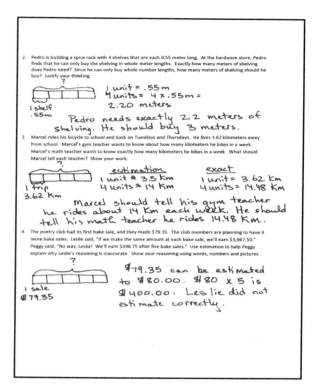

## Exit Ticket  (3 minutes)

After the Student Debrief, instruct students to complete the Exit Ticket. A review of their work will help with assessing students' understanding of the concepts that were presented in today's lesson and planning more effectively for future lessons. The questions may be read aloud to the students.

Lesson 12:    Multiply a decimal fraction by single-digit whole numbers, including using estimation to confirm the placement of the decimal point.

181

# A

Number Correct: _____

Add Decimals

| | | |
|---|---|---|
| 1. | 3 + 1 = | |
| 2. | 3.5 + 1 = | |
| 3. | 3.52 + 1 = | |
| 4. | 0.3 + 0.1 = | |
| 5. | 0.37 + 0.1 = | |
| 6. | 5.37 + 0.1 = | |
| 7. | 0.03 + 0.01 = | |
| 8. | 0.83 + 0.01 = | |
| 9. | 2.83 + 0.01 = | |
| 10. | 30 + 10 = | |
| 11. | 32 + 10 = | |
| 12. | 32.5 + 10 = | |
| 13. | 32.58 + 10 = | |
| 14. | 40.789 + 1 = | |
| 15. | 4 + 1 = | |
| 16. | 4.6 + 1 = | |
| 17. | 4.62 + 1 = | |
| 18. | 4.628 + 1 = | |
| 19. | 4.628 + 0.1 = | |
| 20. | 4.628 + 0.01 = | |
| 21. | 4.628 + 0.001 = | |
| 22. | 27.048 + 0.1 = | |

| | | |
|---|---|---|
| 23. | 5 + 0.1 = | |
| 24. | 5.7 + 0.1 = | |
| 25. | 5.73 + 0.1 = | |
| 26. | 5.736 + 0.1 = | |
| 27. | 5.736 + 1 = | |
| 28. | 5.736 + 0.01 = | |
| 29. | 5.736 + 0.001 = | |
| 30. | 6.208 + 0.01 = | |
| 31. | 3 + 0.01 = | |
| 32. | 3.5 + 0.01 = | |
| 33. | 3.58 + 0.01 = | |
| 34. | 3.584 + 0.01 = | |
| 35. | 3.584 + 0.001 = | |
| 36. | 3.584 + 0.1 = | |
| 37. | 3.584 + 1 = | |
| 38. | 6.804 + 0.01 = | |
| 39. | 8.642 + 0.001 = | |
| 40. | 7.65 + 0.001 = | |
| 41. | 3.987 + 0.1 = | |
| 42. | 4.279 + 0.001 = | |
| 43. | 13.579 + 0.01 = | |
| 44. | 15.491 + 0.01 = | |

Lesson 12:  Multiply a decimal fraction by single-digit whole numbers, including using estimation to confirm the placement of the decimal point.

EUREKA
MATH

# B

Number Correct: _____

Improvement: _____

Add Decimals

| 1. | 2 + 1 = | |
|---|---|---|
| 2. | 2.5 + 1 = | |
| 3. | 2.53 + 1 = | |
| 4. | 0.2 + 0.1 = | |
| 5. | 0.27 + 0.1 = | |
| 6. | 5.27 + 0.1 = | |
| 7. | 0.02 + 0.01 = | |
| 8. | 0.82 + 0.01 = | |
| 9. | 4.82 + 0.01 = | |
| 10. | 20 + 10 = | |
| 11. | 23 + 10 = | |
| 12. | 23.5 + 10 = | |
| 13. | 23.58 + 10 = | |
| 14. | 30.789 + 1 = | |
| 15. | 3 + 1 = | |
| 16. | 3.6 + 1 = | |
| 17. | 3.62 + 1 = | |
| 18. | 3.628 + 1 = | |
| 19. | 3.628 + 0.1 = | |
| 20. | 3.628 + 0.01 = | |
| 21. | 3.628 + 0.001 = | |
| 22. | 37.048 + 0.1 = | |

| 23. | 4 + 0.1 = | |
|---|---|---|
| 24. | 4.7 + 0.1 = | |
| 25. | 4.73 + 0.1 = | |
| 26. | 4.736 + 0.1 = | |
| 27. | 4.736 + 1 = | |
| 28. | 4.736 + 0.01 = | |
| 29. | 4.736 + 0.001 = | |
| 30. | 5.208 + 0.01 = | |
| 31. | 2 + 0.01 = | |
| 32. | 2.5 + 0.01 = | |
| 33. | 2.58 + 0.01 = | |
| 34. | 2.584 + 0.01 = | |
| 35. | 2.584 + 0.001 = | |
| 36. | 2.584 + 0.1 = | |
| 37. | 2.584 + 1 = | |
| 38. | 5.804 + 0.01 = | |
| 39. | 7.642 + 0.001 = | |
| 40. | 6.75 + 0.001 = | |
| 41. | 2.987 + 0.1 = | |
| 42. | 3.279 + 0.001 = | |
| 43. | 12.579 + 0.01 = | |
| 44. | 14.391 + 0.01 = | |

Name _____     Date _____

1. Choose the reasonable product for each expression. Explain your reasoning in the spaces below using words, pictures, or numbers.

   a.  2.5 × 4                 0.1          1          10          100

   _____

   b.  3.14 × 7               2198       219.8       21.98       2.198

   _____

   c.  8 × 6.022             4.8176      48.176     481.76      4817.6

   _____

   d.  9 × 5.48              493.2       49.32      4.932       0.4932

© 2015 Great Minds. eureka-math.org
G5-M1-TE-B1-1.3.1-1.2016

**EUREKA MATH**

2. Pedro is building a spice rack with 4 shelves that are each 0.55 meter long. At the hardware store, Pedro finds that he can only buy the shelving in whole meter lengths. Exactly how many meters of shelving does Pedro need? Since he can only buy whole-number lengths, how many meters of shelving should he buy? Justify your thinking.

3. Marcel rides his bicycle to school and back on Tuesdays and Thursdays. He lives 3.62 kilometers away from school. Marcel's gym teacher wants to know about how many kilometers he bikes in a week. Marcel's math teacher wants to know exactly how many kilometers he bikes in a week. What should Marcel tell each teacher? Show your work.

4. The poetry club had its first bake sale, and they made $79.35. The club members are planning to have 4 more bake sales. Leslie said, "If we make the same amount at each bake sale, we'll earn $3,967.50." Peggy said, "No way, Leslie! We'll earn $396.75 after five bake sales." Use estimation to help Peggy explain why Leslie's reasoning is inaccurate. Show your reasoning using words, numbers, or pictures.

Lesson 12:    Multiply a decimal fraction by single-digit whole numbers, including using estimation to confirm the placement of the decimal point.

185

© 2015 Great Minds. eureka-math.org
G5-M1-TE-B1-1.3.1-1.2016

Name _____     Date _____

1.  Use estimation to choose the correct value for each expression.

    a.  5.1 × 2          0.102          1.02          10.2          102

    b.  4 × 8.93         3.572          35.72         357.2         3572

2.  Estimate the answer for 7.13 × 6. Explain your reasoning using words, pictures, or numbers.

**Lesson 12:**     Multiply a decimal fraction by single-digit whole numbers, including
                   using estimation to confirm the placement of the decimal point.

EUREKA
MATH

Name _____  Date _____

1. Choose the reasonable product for each expression. Explain your thinking in the spaces below using words, pictures, or numbers.

   a.  $2.1 \times 3$          0.63      6.3      63      630

   _____

   b.  $4.27 \times 6$         2562      256.2    25.62    2.562

   _____

   c.  $7 \times 6.053$        4237.1    423.71   42.371   4.2371

   _____

   d.  $9 \times 4.82$         4.338     43.38    433.8    4338

Lesson 12: Multiply a decimal fraction by single-digit whole numbers, including using estimation to confirm the placement of the decimal point.

187

© 2015 Great Minds. eureka-math.org
G5-M1-TE-B1-1.3.1-1.2016

2. Yi Ting weighs 8.3 kg. Her older brother is 4 times as heavy as Yi Ting. How much does her older brother weigh in kilograms?

3. Tim is painting his storage shed. He buys 4 gallons of white paint and 3 gallons of blue paint. Each gallon of white paint costs $15.72, and each gallon of blue paint is $21.87. How much will Tim spend in all on paint?

4. Ribbon is sold at 3 yards for $6.33. Jackie bought 24 yards of ribbon for a project. How much did she pay?

Lesson 12: Multiply a decimal fraction by single-digit whole numbers, including using estimation to confirm the placement of the decimal point.

EUREKA
MATH

5
GRADE

# Mathematics Curriculum

Topic F
# Dividing Decimals

## 5.NBT.3, 5.NBT.7

| Focus Standards: | 5.NBT.3 | Read, write, and compare decimals to thousandths. |
|---|---|---|
| | | a. Read and write decimals to thousandths using base-ten numerals, number names, and expanded form, e.g., 347.392 = 3 × 100 + 4 × 10 + 7 × 1 + 3 × (1/10) + 9 × (1/100) + 2 × (1/1000). |
| | | b. Compare two decimals to thousandths based on meanings of the digits in each place, using >, =, and < symbols to record the results of comparisons. |
| | 5.NBT.7 | Add, subtract, multiply, and divide decimals to hundredths, using concrete models or drawings and strategies based on place value, properties of operations, and/or the relationship between addition and subtraction; relate the strategy to a written method and explain the reasoning used. |
| Instructional Days: | 4 | |
| Coherence  -Links from: | G4–M3 | Multi-Digit Multiplication and Division |
| -Links to: | G5–M2 | Multi-Digit Whole Number and Decimal Fraction Operations |
| | G6–M2 | Arithmetic Operations Including Dividing by a Fraction |

Topic F concludes Module 1 with an exploration of division of decimal numbers by one-digit whole-number divisors using place value charts and disks. Lessons begin with easily identifiable multiples such as 4.2 ÷ 6 and move to quotients that have a remainder in the smallest unit (through the thousandths). Written methods for decimal cases are related to place value strategies, properties of operations, and familiar written methods for whole numbers (**5.NBT.7**). Students solidify their skills with an understanding of the algorithm before moving on to division involving two-digit divisors in Module 2. Students apply their accumulated knowledge of decimal operations to solve word problems at the close of the module.

**Topic F:**      Dividing Decimals

**189**

| A Teaching Sequence Toward Mastery of Dividing Decimals |
| --- |

**Objective 1:** Divide decimals by single-digit whole numbers involving easily identifiable multiples using place value understanding and relate to a written method.
(Lesson 13)

**Objective 2:** Divide decimals with a remainder using place value understanding and relate to a written method.
(Lesson 14)

**Objective 3:** Divide decimals using place value understanding including remainders in the smallest unit.
(Lesson 15)

**Objective 4:** Solve word problems using decimal operations.
(Lesson 16)

© 2015 Great Minds. eureka-math.org
G5-M1-TE-B1-1.3.1-1.2016

# Lesson 13

Objective: Divide decimals by single-digit whole numbers involving easily identifiable multiples using place value understanding and relate to a written method.

## Suggested Lesson Structure

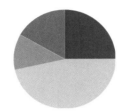

■ Fluency Practice          (15 minutes)
■ Application Problem        (7 minutes)
□ Concept Development       (28 minutes)
■ Student Debrief           (10 minutes)

**Total Time**              **(60 minutes)**

## Fluency Practice  (15 minutes)

- Sprint:  Subtract Decimals  **5.NBT.7**          (9 minutes)
- Find the Product  **5.NBT.7**                    (3 minutes)
- Compare Decimal Fractions  **3.NF.3d**           (3 minutes)

### Sprint:  Subtract Decimals  (9 minutes)

Materials:   (S) Subtract Decimals Sprint

Note:  This Sprint helps students build automaticity in subtracting decimals without renaming.

### Find the Product  (3 minutes)

Materials:   (S) Personal white board

Note:  Reviewing this skill introduced in Lessons 11–12 helps students work toward mastery of multiplying single-digit numbers times decimals.

    T:   (Write $4 \times 3 =$ ___.) Say the multiplication sentence in unit form.
    S:   $4 \times 3$ ones = 12 ones.
    T:   (Write $4 \times 0.2 =$ ___.) Say the multiplication sentence in unit form.
    S:   $4 \times 2$ tenths = 8 tenths.
    T:   (Write $4 \times 3.2 =$ ___.) Say the multiplication sentence in unit form.
    S:   $4 \times 3$ ones 2 tenths = 12 and 8 tenths.

Lesson 13:    Divide decimals by single-digit whole numbers involving easily
identifiable multiples using place value understanding and relate
to a written method.

191

T:   Write the multiplication sentence.

S:   (Write 4 × 3.2 = 12.8.)

Repeat the process for 4 × 3.21, 9 × 2, 9 × 0.1, 9 × 0.03, 9 × 2.13, 4.012 × 4, and 5 × 3.237.

## Compare Decimal Fractions  (3 minutes)

Materials:    (S) Personal white board

Note:  This review fluency helps solidify student understanding of place value in the decimal system.

T:   (Write 13.78 ___ 13.86.) On your personal white boards, compare the numbers using the greater than, less than, or equal sign.

S:   (Write 13.78 < 13.86.)

Repeat the process and procedure for 0.78 ___ $\frac{78}{100}$, 439.3 ___ 4.39, 5.08 ___ fifty-eight tenths, thirty-five and 9 thousandths ___ 4 tens.

## Application Problem  (7 minutes)

Louis buys 4 chocolates. Each chocolate costs $2.35. Louis multiplies 4 × 235 and gets 940. Place the decimal to show the cost of the chocolates, and explain your reasoning using words, numbers, and pictures.

Note:  This Application Problem requires students to estimate 4 × $2.35 in order to place the decimal point in the product. This skill was taught in Lesson 12.

He paid $9.40 for the chocolates. The decimal has to go between the 9 and 4 because when Louis multiplies 4 and 235 it means 940 hundredths which is 9 wholes and 40 hundredths.

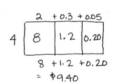

The only place that makes sense is between the 9 and 4 because He will pay between (4 x $2) and (4 x $3).

## Concept Development  (28 minutes)

Materials:    (S) Hundreds to thousandths place value chart (Lesson 7 Template), personal white board

**Problems 1–3**

0.9 ÷ 3 = 0.3

0.24 ÷ 4 = 0.06

0.032 ÷ 8 = 0.004

T:   Draw disks to show 9 tenths on your hundreds to thousandths place value chart.

S:   (Show.)

T:   Divide 9 tenths into 3 equal groups.

S:   (Make 3 groups of 3 tenths.)

T:   How many tenths are in each group?

Lesson 13:   Divide decimals by single-digit whole numbers involving easily identifiable multiples using place value understanding and relate to a written method.

EUREKA MATH

S:  There are 3 tenths in each group.

T:  (Write 0.9 ÷ 3 = 0.3 on the board.) Read the number sentence using unit form.

S:  9 tenths divided by 3 equals 3 tenths.

T:  How does unit form help us divide?

S:  When we identify the units, then it's just like dividing 9 apples into 3 groups. → If you know what unit you are sharing, then it's just like whole-number division. You can just think about the basic fact.

T:  (Write 3 groups of _____ = 0.9 on the board.) What is the unknown in our number sentence?

S:  3 tenths (0.3).

Repeat this sequence with 0.24 ÷ 4 = 0.06 (24 hundredths divided by 4 equals 6 hundredths) and 0.032 ÷ 8 = 0.004 (32 thousandths divided by 8 equals 4 thousandths).

**Problems 4–6**

1.5 ÷ 5 = 0.3

1.05 ÷ 5 = 0.21

3.015 ÷ 5 = 0.603

T:  (Write on the board 1.5 ÷ 5.) Read the equation stating the whole in unit form.

S:  Fifteen tenths divided by 5.

T:  What is useful about reading the decimal as 15 tenths?

S:  When you say the units, it's like a basic fact.

T:  What is 15 tenths divided by 5?

S:  3 tenths.

T:  (On the board, complete the equation 1.5 ÷ 5 = 0.3.)

T:  (On the board, write 1.05 ÷ 5.) Read the expression using unit form for the dividend.

S:  105 hundredths divided by 5.

T:  Is there another way to decompose (name or group) this quantity?

S:  1 one and 5 hundredths. → 10 tenths and 5 hundredths.

T:  Which way of naming 1.05 is most useful when dividing by 5? Why? Turn and talk, and then solve.

S:  10 tenths and 5 hundredths because they are both multiples of 5. This makes it easy to use basic facts to divide mentally. The answer is 2 tenths and 1 hundredth. → 105 hundredths is easier for me because I know 100 is 20 fives, so 105 is 1 more: 21. 21 hundredths. → I just used the algorithm from Grade 4 and got 21. I knew it was hundredths.

> ### NOTES ON MULTIPLE MEANS OF ENGAGEMENT:
>
> Students can also be challenged to use a compensation strategy to make another connection to whole-number division. The dividend is multiplied by a power of ten, which converts it to its smallest units. Once the dividend is shared among the groups, it must be converted back to the original units by dividing it by the same power of ten. For example:
>
> 1.5 ÷ 5 → (1.5 × 10) ÷ 5 →
>
> 15 ÷ 5 = 3 → 3 ÷ 10 = 0.3

Repeat this sequence with 3.015 ÷ 5. Have students decompose the decimal several ways and then reason about which is the most useful for division. It is also important to draw parallels among the next three problems. Lead students by asking questions such as "How does the answer to the second set of problems help you find the answer to the third?" if necessary.

Lesson 13:   Divide decimals by single-digit whole numbers involving easily identifiable multiples using place value understanding and relate to a written method.

193

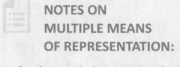

## Problems 7–9

Compare the relationships between:

4.8 ÷ 6 = 0.8 and 48 ÷ 6 = 8

4.08 ÷ 8 = 0.51 and 408 ÷ 8 = 51

63.021 ÷ 7 = 9.003 and 63,021 ÷ 7 = 9,003

> **NOTES ON MULTIPLE MEANS OF REPRESENTATION:**
>
> Unfamiliar vocabulary can slow down the learning process or even confuse students. Reviewing key vocabulary, such as *dividend*, *divisor*, or *quotient*, may benefit all students. Displaying the words in a familiar mathematical sentence may serve as a useful reference for students. For example, display:
>
> Dividend ÷ Divisor = Quotient.

- T:  (Write 4.8 ÷ 6 = 0.8 and 48 ÷ 6 = 8 on the board.) What relationships do you notice between these two equations? How are they alike?

- S:  8 is 10 times greater than 0.8. → 48 is 10 times greater than 4.8. → The digits are the same in both equations, but the decimal points are in different places.

- T:  How can 48 ÷ 6 help you with 4.8 ÷ 6? Turn and talk.

- S:  If you think of the basic fact first, then you can get a quick answer. Then, you just have to remember what units were really in the problem. This one was really 48 tenths. → The division is the same; the units are the only difference.

Repeat the process for 4.08 ÷ 8 = 0.51 and 408 ÷ 8 = 51, 63.021 ÷ 7 = 9.003, and 63,021 ÷ 7 = 9,003.

- T:  When completing the Problem Set, remember to use what you know about whole numbers to help you divide the decimal numbers.

## Problem Set  (10 minutes)

Students should do their personal best to complete the Problem Set within the allotted 10 minutes. For some classes, it may be appropriate to modify the assignment by specifying which problems they work on first. Some problems do not specify a method for solving. Students solve these problems using the RDW approach used for Application Problems.

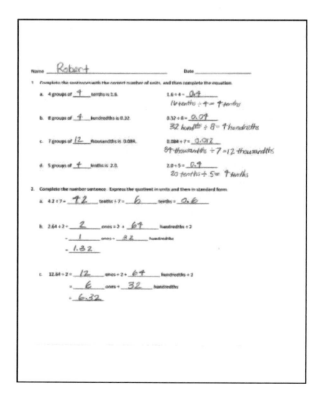

## Student Debrief  (10 minutes)

**Lesson Objective:**  Divide decimals by single-digit whole numbers involving easily identifiable multiples using place value understanding and relate to a written method.

The Student Debrief is intended to invite reflection and active processing of the total lesson experience.

Lesson 13:   Divide decimals by single-digit whole numbers involving easily identifiable multiples using place value understanding and relate to a written method.

© 2015 Great Minds. eureka-math.org
G5-M1-TE-B1-1.3.1-1.2016

**EUREKA MATH**

Invite students to review their solutions for the Problem Set. They should check work by comparing answers with a partner before going over answers as a class. Look for misconceptions or misunderstandings that can be addressed in the Debrief. Guide students in a conversation to debrief the Problem Set and process the lesson.

Any combination of the questions below may be used to lead the discussion.

- In Problem 2(a), how does your understanding of whole-number division help you solve the equation with a decimal?

- Is there another decomposition of the dividend in Problem 2(c) that could have been useful in dividing by 2? What about in Problem 2(d)? Why or why not?

- When decomposing decimals in different ways, how can you tell which is the most useful? (We are looking for easily identifiable multiples of the divisor.)

- In Problem 4(a), what mistake is being made that would produce $5.6 \div 7 = 8$?

- Change the dividends in Problem 4 so that all of the quotients are correct. Is there a pattern to the changes that you must make?

- $4.221 \div 7 =$ _____. Explain how you would decompose 4.221 so that you only need knowledge of basic facts to find the quotient.

## Exit Ticket  (3 minutes)

After the Student Debrief, instruct students to complete the Exit Ticket. A review of their work will help with assessing students' understanding of the concepts that were presented in today's lesson and planning more effectively for future lessons. The questions may be read aloud to the students.

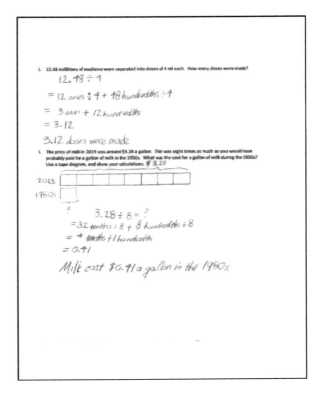

Lesson 13:   Divide decimals by single-digit whole numbers involving easily identifiable multiples using place value understanding and relate to a written method.

195

# A

Number Correct: _____

Subtract Decimals

| 1. | 5 – 1 = | | | 23. | 7.985 – 0.002 = | |
|---|---|---|---|---|---|---|
| 2. | 5.9 – 1 = | | | 24. | 7.985 – 0.004 = | |
| 3. | 5.93 – 1 = | | | 25. | 2.7 – 0.1 = | |
| 4. | 5.932 – 1 = | | | 26. | 2.785 – 0.1 = | |
| 5. | 5.932 – 2 = | | | 27. | 2.785 – 0.5 = | |
| 6. | 5.932 – 4 = | | | 28. | 4.913 – 0.4 = | |
| 7. | 0.5 – 0.1 = | | | 29. | 3.58 – 0.01 = | |
| 8. | 0.53 – 0.1 = | | | 30. | 3.586 – 0.01 = | |
| 9. | 0.539 – 0.1 = | | | 31. | 3.586 – 0.05 = | |
| 10. | 8.539 – 0.1 = | | | 32. | 7.982 – 0.04 = | |
| 11. | 8.539 – 0.2 = | | | 33. | 6.126 – 0.001 = | |
| 12. | 8.539 – 0.4 = | | | 34. | 6.126 – 0.004 = | |
| 13. | 0.05 – 0.01 = | | | 35. | 9.348 – 0.006 = | |
| 14. | 0.057 – 0.01 = | | | 36. | 8.347 – 0.3 = | |
| 15. | 1.057 – 0.01 = | | | 37. | 9.157 – 0.05 = | |
| 16. | 1.857 – 0.01 = | | | 38. | 6.879 – 0.009 = | |
| 17. | 1.857 – 0.02 = | | | 39. | 6.548 – 2 = | |
| 18. | 1.857 – 0.04 = | | | 40. | 6.548 – 0.2 = | |
| 19. | 0.005 – 0.001 = | | | 41. | 6.548 – 0.02 = | |
| 20. | 7.005 – 0.001 = | | | 42. | 6.548 – 0.002 = | |
| 21. | 7.905 – 0.001 = | | | 43. | 6.196 – 0.06 = | |
| 22. | 7.985 – 0.001 = | | | 44. | 9.517 – 0.004 = | |

Lesson 13: Divide decimals by single-digit whole numbers involving easily identifiable multiples using place value understanding and relate to a written method.

© 2015 Great Minds. eureka-math.org
G5-M1-TE-B1-1.3.1-1.2016

EUREKA MATH

# B

Number Correct: _____

Improvement: _____

Subtract Decimals

| | | |
|---|---|---|
| 1. | 6 – 1 = | |
| 2. | 6.9 – 1 = | |
| 3. | 6.93 – 1 = | |
| 4. | 6.932 – 1 = | |
| 5. | 6.932 – 2 = | |
| 6. | 6.932 – 4 = | |
| 7. | 0.6 – 0.1 = | |
| 8. | 0.63 – 0.1 = | |
| 9. | 0.639 – 0.1 = | |
| 10. | 8.639 – 0.1 = | |
| 11. | 8.639 – 0.2 = | |
| 12. | 8.639 – 0.4 = | |
| 13. | 0.06 – 0.01 = | |
| 14. | 0.067 – 0.01 = | |
| 15. | 1.067 – 0.01 = | |
| 16. | 1.867 – 0.01 = | |
| 17. | 1.867 – 0.02 = | |
| 18. | 1.867 – 0.04 = | |
| 19. | 0.006 – 0.001 = | |
| 20. | 7.006 – 0.001 = | |
| 21. | 7.906 – 0.001 = | |
| 22. | 7.986 – 0.001 = | |

| | | |
|---|---|---|
| 23. | 7.986 – 0.002 = | |
| 24. | 7.986 – 0.004 = | |
| 25. | 3.7 – 0.1 = | |
| 26. | 3.785 – 0.1 = | |
| 27. | 3.785 – 0.5 = | |
| 28. | 5.924 – 0.4 = | |
| 29. | 4.58 – 0.01 = | |
| 30. | 4.586 – 0.01 = | |
| 31. | 4.586 – 0.05 = | |
| 32. | 6.183 – 0.04 = | |
| 33. | 7.127 – 0.001 = | |
| 34. | 7.127 – 0.004 = | |
| 35. | 1.459 – 0.006 = | |
| 36. | 8.457 – 0.4 = | |
| 37. | 1.267 – 0.06 = | |
| 38. | 7.981 – 0.001 = | |
| 39. | 7.548 – 2 = | |
| 40. | 7.548 – 0.2 = | |
| 41. | 7.548 – 0.02 = | |
| 42. | 7.548 – 0.002 = | |
| 43. | 7.197 – 0.06 = | |
| 44. | 1.627 – 0.004 = | |

**Lesson 13:** Divide decimals by single-digit whole numbers involving easily identifiable multiples using place value understanding and relate to a written method.

197

© 2015 Great Minds. eureka-math.org
G5-M1-TE-B1-1.3.1-1.2016

Name _____      Date _____

1. Complete the sentences with the correct number of units, and then complete the equation.

   a. 4 groups of _____ tenths is 1.6.         $1.6 \div 4 =$ _____

   b. 8 groups of _____ hundredths is 0.32.     $0.32 \div 8 =$ _____

   c. 7 groups of _____ thousandths is 0.084.    $0.084 \div 7 =$ _____

   d. 5 groups of _____ tenths is 2.0.        $2.0 \div 5 =$ _____

2. Complete the number sentence. Express the quotient in units and then in standard form.

   a. $4.2 \div 7 =$ _____ tenths $\div 7 =$ _____ tenths $=$ _____

   b. $2.64 \div 2 =$ _____ ones $\div 2 +$ _____ hundredths $\div 2$

          $=$ _____ ones $+$ _____ hundredths

          $=$ _____

   c. $12.64 \div 2 =$ _____ ones $\div 2 +$ _____ hundredths $\div 2$

          $=$ _____ ones $+$ _____ hundredths

          $=$ _____

   d. $4.26 \div 6 =$ _____ tenths $\div 6 +$ _____ hundredths $\div 6$

          $=$ _____

          $=$ _____

     **Lesson 13:**    Divide decimals by single-digit whole numbers involving easily
                       identifiable multiples using place value understanding and relate
                       to a written method.

© 2015 Great Minds. eureka-math.org
G5-M1-TE-B1-1.3.1-1.2016

**EUREKA MATH**

e.   4.236 ÷ 6 = _____

     = _____

     = _____

3.  Find the quotients. Then, use words, numbers, or pictures to describe any relationships you notice between each pair of problems and quotients.

    a.   32 ÷ 8 = _____          3.2 ÷ 8 = _____

    b.   81 ÷ 9 = _____          0.081 ÷ 9 = _____

4.  Are the quotients below reasonable? Explain your answers.

    a.   5.6 ÷ 7 = 8

    b.   56 ÷ 7 = 0.8

    c.   0.56 ÷ 7 = 0.08

**Lesson 13:**   Divide decimals by single-digit whole numbers involving easily identifiable multiples using place value understanding and relate to a written method.

199

5.  12.48 milliliters of medicine were separated into doses of 4 mL each. How many doses were made?

6.  The price of milk in 2013 was around $3.28 a gallon. This was eight times as much as you would have probably paid for a gallon of milk in the 1950s. What was the cost for a gallon of milk during the 1950s? Use a tape diagram, and show your calculations.

Lesson 13:    Divide decimals by single-digit whole numbers involving easily identifiable multiples using place value understanding and relate to a written method.

© 2015 Great Minds. eureka-math.org
G5-M1-TE-B1-1.3.1-1.2016

EUREKA
MATH

Name _____ Date _____

1. Complete the sentences with the correct number of units, and then complete the equation.

    a. 2 groups of _____ tenths is 1.8.                    $1.8 \div 2 =$ _____

    b. 4 groups of _____ hundredths is 0.32.              $0.32 \div 4 =$ _____

    c. 7 groups of _____ thousandths is 0.021.           $0.021 \div 7 =$ _____

2. Complete the number sentence. Express the quotient in unit form and then in standard form.

    a. $4.5 \div 5 =$ _____ tenths $\div 5 =$ _____ tenths = _____

    b. $6.12 \div 6 =$ _____ ones $\div 6 +$ _____ hundredths $\div 6$

       = _____ ones + _____ hundredths

       = _____

EUREKA
MATH

Lesson 13:   Divide decimals by single-digit whole numbers involving easily
            identifiable multiples using place value understanding and relate
            to a written method.

201

© 2015 Great Minds. eureka-math.org
G5-M1-TE-B1-1.3.1-1.2016

Name _____ Date _____

1. Complete the sentences with the correct number of units, and then complete the equation.

   a. 3 groups of _____ tenths is 1.5.               1.5 ÷ 3 = _____

   b. 6 groups of _____ hundredths is 0.24.          0.24 ÷ 6 = _____

   c. 5 groups of _____ thousandths is 0.045.        0.045 ÷ 5 = _____

2. Complete the number sentence. Express the quotient in units and then in standard form.

   a. 9.36 ÷ 3 = _____ ones ÷ 3 + _____ hundredths ÷ 3

      = _____ ones + _____ hundredths

      = _____

   b. 36.012 ÷ 3 = _____ ones ÷ 3 + _____ thousandths ÷ 3

      = _____ ones + _____ thousandths

      = _____

   c. 3.55 ÷ 5 = _____ tenths ÷ 5 + _____ hundredths ÷ 5

      = _____

      = _____

   d. 3.545 ÷ 5 = _____

      = _____

      = _____

Lesson 13: Divide decimals by single-digit whole numbers involving easily identifiable multiples using place value understanding and relate to a written method.

© 2015 Great Minds. eureka-math.org
G5-M1-TE-B1-1.3.1-1.2016

EUREKA MATH

3. Find the quotients. Then, use words, numbers, or pictures to describe any relationships you notice between each pair of problems and quotients.

   a. 21 ÷ 7 = _____          2.1 ÷ 7 = _____

   b. 48 ÷ 8 = _____          0.048 ÷ 8 = _____

4. Are the quotients below reasonable? Explain your answers.

   a. 0.54 ÷ 6 = 9

   b. 5.4 ÷ 6 = 0.9

   c. 54 ÷ 6 = 0.09

 EUREKA MATH

Lesson 13: Divide decimals by single-digit whole numbers involving easily identifiable multiples using place value understanding and relate to a written method.

203

© 2015 Great Minds. eureka-math.org
G5-M1-TE-B1-1.3.1-1.2016

5. A toy airplane costs $4.84. It costs 4 times as much as a toy car. What is the cost of the toy car?

6. Julian bought 3.9 liters of cranberry juice, and Jay bought 8.74 liters of apple juice. They mixed the two juices together and then poured them equally into 2 bottles. How many liters of juice are in each bottle?

Lesson 13: Divide decimals by single-digit whole numbers involving easily identifiable multiples using place value understanding and relate to a written method.

© 2015 Great Minds. eureka-math.org
G5-M1-TE-B1-1.3.1-1.2016

# Lesson 14

Objective:  Divide decimals with a remainder using place value understanding and relate to a written method.

## Suggested Lesson Structure

■ Fluency Practice          (12 minutes)
■ Application Problem      (8 minutes)
■ Concept Development     (30 minutes)
■ Student Debrief          (10 minutes)
   **Total Time**           **(60 minutes)**

## Fluency Practice  (12 minutes)

- Multiply and Divide by Exponents  **5.NBT.2**      (3 minutes)
- Round to Different Place Values  **5.NBT.4**       (3 minutes)
- Find the Quotient  **5.NBT.5**                     (6 minutes)

### Multiply and Divide by Exponents  (3 minutes)

Materials:   (T) Millions to thousandths place value chart (Lesson 1 Template 2)  (S) Millions to thousandths place value chart (Lesson 1 Template 2), personal white board

Note:  This review fluency helps solidify student understanding of multiplying by 10, 100, and 1,000 in the decimal system.

　T:   (Project the place value chart from millions to thousandths.) Using the place value chart, write 65 tenths as a decimal.

　S:   (Write 6 in the ones column and 5 in the tenths column.)

　T:   Say the decimal.

　S:   6.5

　T:   Multiply it by $10^2$.

　S:   (Cross out 6.5 and write 650.)

Repeat the process and sequence for $0.7 \times 10^2$, $0.8 \div 10^2$, $3.895 \times 10^3$, and $5,472 \div 10^3$.

Lesson 14:    Divide decimals with a remainder using place value understanding
              and relate to a written method.

205

© 2015 Great Minds. eureka-math.org
G5-M1-TE-B1-1.3.1-1.2016

## Round to Different Place Values  (3 minutes)

Materials:   (S) Personal white board

Note:  This review fluency helps solidify student understanding of rounding decimals to different place values.

- T:   (Project 6.385.) Say the number.
- S:   6 and 385 thousandths.
- T:   On your personal white boards, round the number to the nearest tenth.
- S:   (Write 6.385 ≈ 6.4.)

Repeat the process, rounding 6.385 and 37.645 to the nearest hundredth.

## Find the Quotient  (6 minutes)

Materials:   (S) Personal white board

Note:  Reviewing these skills introduced in Lesson 13 helps students work toward mastery of dividing decimals by single-digit whole numbers.

- T:   (Write 14 ÷ 2 = _____.) Write the division sentence.
- S:   14 ÷ 2 = 7.
- T:   Say the division sentence in unit form.
- S:   14 ones ÷ 2 = 7 ones.

Repeat the process for 1.4 ÷ 2, 0.14 ÷ 2, 24 ÷ 3, 2.4 ÷ 3, 0.24 ÷ 3, 30 ÷ 3, 3 ÷ 3, and 0.3 ÷ 3.

## Application Problem  (8 minutes)

A bag of potato chips contains 0.96 grams of sodium. If the bag is split into 8 equal servings, how many grams of sodium will each serving contain?

Extension:  What other ways can the bag be divided into equal servings so that the amount of sodium in each serving has two digits to the right of the decimal and the digits are greater than zero in the tenths and hundredths place?

Note:  This Application Problem reviews dividing decimal numbers by a single-digit whole number.

$0.96 \div 8$

$= 96$ hundredths $\div 8$

$= 12$ hundredths

$= 0.12$

Each serving will contain 0.12g of Sodium.

Extension:

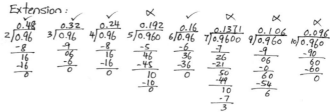

96 can be divided by:

2 ⟶ 0.48g ✓

3 ⟶ 0.32g ✓

4 ⟶ 0.24g ✓

5 ⟶ 0.192g ✗

6 ⟶ 0.16g

7 ⟶ too many decimal ✗ places

9 ⟶ too many decimal ✗ places

10 ⟶ less than 0.11 ✗

EUREKA MATH

## Concept Development (30 minutes)

Materials: (S) Hundreds to thousandths place value chart (Lesson 7 Template), place value disks, personal white board

**Problem 1**

6.72 ÷ 3 = _____

5.16 ÷ 4 = _____

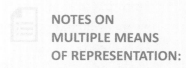

**NOTES ON MULTIPLE MEANS OF REPRESENTATION:**

In order to activate prior knowledge, have students solve one or two whole-number division problems using the place value disks. Help them record their work, step by step, in the standard algorithm. This may help students understand that division of whole numbers and the division of decimal fractions are the same concept and process.

T: (Write 6.72 ÷ 3 = _____ on the board, and draw a place value chart with 3 groups at the bottom.) Show 6.72 on your place value chart using your place value disks. I'll draw on my chart.

S: (Represent work with the place value disks.)

For the first problem, students show their work with the place value disks. The teacher will represent the work in a drawing and in the algorithm. In Problems 2 and 3 of the Concept Development, students may draw instead of using the disks.

T: Let's begin with our largest units. We will share 6 ones equally with 3 groups. How many ones are in each group?

S: 2 ones. (Move the place value disks to show the distribution.)

T: (Draw 2 place value disks in each group, and cross off in the dividend as they are shared.) We gave each group 2 ones. (In the algorithm, record 2 in the ones place in the quotient.) How many ones did we share in all?

S: 6 ones.

T: (Show the subtraction in the algorithm.) How many ones are left to share?

S: 0 ones.

T: Let's share our tenths. 7 tenths divided by 3. How many tenths can we share with each group?

S: 2 tenths.

T: Using your place value disks, share your tenths. I'll show what we did on my place value chart and in my written work. (Draw to share and cross off in the dividend. Record in the algorithm.)

S: (Move the place value disks.)

T: (Record 2 in the tenths place in the quotient.) How many tenths did we share in all?

S: 6 tenths.

T: (Record subtraction.) Let's stop here a moment. Why are we subtracting the 6 tenths?

S: We have to take away the tenths we have already shared. → We distributed the 6 tenths into 3 groups, so we have to subtract them.

T: Since we shared 6 tenths in all, how many tenths are left to share?

Lesson 14: Divide decimals with a remainder using place value understanding and relate to a written method.

207

© 2015 Great Minds. eureka-math.org
G5-M1-TE-B1-1.3.1-1.2016

S:   1 tenth.

T:   Can we share 1 tenth with 3 groups?

S:   No.

T:   What can we do to keep sharing?

S:   We can change 1 tenth for 10 hundredths.

**MP.6**

T:   Make that exchange on your place value chart. I'll record.

T:   How many hundredths do we have now?

S:   12 hundredths.

T:   Can we share 12 hundredths with 3 groups? If so, how many hundredths can we share with each group?

S:   Yes. We can give 4 hundredths to each group.

T:   Share your hundredths, and I'll record.

T:   (Record 4 hundredths in the quotient.) Each group received 4 hundredths. How many hundredths did we share in all?

S:   12 hundredths.

T:   (Record subtraction.) Remind me why we subtract these 12 hundredths. How many hundredths are left?

S:   We subtract because those 12 hundredths have been shared. → They are now divided into the groups, so we have to subtract. 12 hundredths minus 12 hundredths is equal to 0 hundredths.

T:   Look at the 3 groups you made. How many are in each group?

S:   2 and 24 hundredths.

T:   Do we have any other units to share?

S:   No.

T:   How is the division we did with decimal units like whole-number division? Turn and talk.

S:   It's the same as dividing whole numbers, except we are sharing units smaller than ones. → Our quotient has a decimal point because we are sharing fractional units. The decimal shows where the ones place is. → Sometimes we have to change the decimal units just like we change the whole-number units in order to continue dividing.

T:   (Write 5.16 ÷ 4 = ____ on the board.) Let's switch jobs for this problem. I will use place value disks. You record using the algorithm.

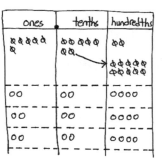

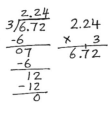

**NOTES ON MULTIPLE MEANS OF ACTION AND EXPRESSION:**

Students should have the opportunity to use tools that will enhance their understanding. In math class, this often means using manipulatives. Communicate to students that the journey from concrete understanding to representational understanding (drawings) to abstraction is rarely a linear one. Create a learning environment in which students feel comfortable returning to concrete manipulatives when problems are challenging. Throughout this module, the place value disks should be readily available to all learners.

Follow the questioning sequence from above. Students record the steps of the algorithm as the teacher models using the place value disks.

Lesson 14:        Divide decimals with a remainder using place value understanding and relate to a written method.

**EUREKA MATH**

## Problem 2

6.72 ÷ 4 = _____

20.08 ÷ 8 = _____

   T:  (Write 6.72 ÷ 4 = _____ on the board.) Using the place value chart, solve this problem with your partner. Partner A will draw the place value disks, and Partner B will record all steps using the standard algorithm.

   S:  (Work to solve.)

   T:  Compare the drawing to the algorithm. Match each number to its counterpart in the drawing.

Circulate to ensure that students are using their whole-number experiences with division to share decimal units. Check for misconceptions in recording. For the second problem in the set, partners should switch roles.

## Problem 3

6.372 ÷ 6 = _____

   T:  (Write 6.372 ÷ 6 = _____ on the board.) Work independently using the standard algorithm to solve.

   S:  (Work to solve.)

   T:  Compare your quotient with your partner's. How is this problem different from the ones in the other Problem Sets? Turn and talk.

## Problem Set  (10 minutes)

Students should do their personal best to complete the Problem Set within the allotted 10 minutes. For some classes, it may be appropriate to modify the assignment by specifying which problems they work on first. Some problems do not specify a method for solving. Students solve these problems using the RDW approach used for Application Problems.

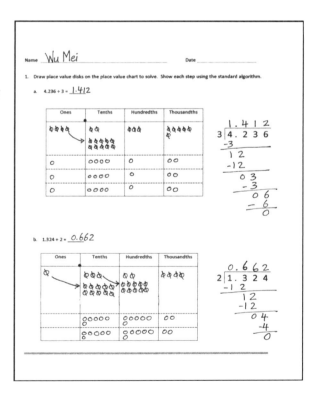

## Student Debrief  (10 minutes)

**Lesson Objective:**  Divide decimals with a remainder using place value understanding and relate to a written method.

The Student Debrief is intended to invite reflection and active processing of the total lesson experience.

Invite students to review their solutions for the Problem Set. They should check work by comparing answers with a partner before going over answers as a class. Look for misconceptions or misunderstandings that can be addressed in the Debrief. Guide students in a conversation to debrief the Problem Set and process the lesson.

Any combination of the questions below may be used to lead the discussion.

- How are dividing decimals and dividing whole numbers similar? How are they different?

- Look at the quotients in Problems 1(a) and 1(b). What do you notice about the values in each of the ones places? Explain why Problem 1(b) has a zero in the ones place.

- Explain your approach to Problem 5. (Because this is a multi-step problem, students may have arrived at the solution through different means. Some may have divided $4.10 by 5 and compared the quotient to the regularly priced avocado. Others may first multiply the regular price, $0.94, by 5, subtract $4.10 from that product, and then divide the difference by 5. Both approaches will result in a correct answer of $0.12 saved per avocado.)

## Exit Ticket  (3 minutes)

After the Student Debrief, instruct students to complete the Exit Ticket. A review of their work will help with assessing students' understanding of the concepts that were presented in today's lesson and planning more effectively for future lessons. The questions may be read aloud to the students.

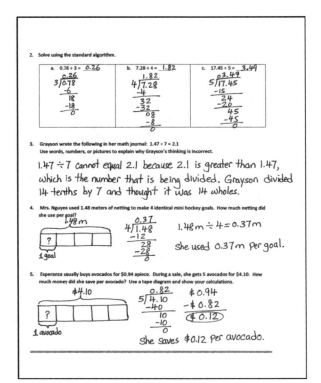

© 2015 Great Minds. eureka-math.org
G5-M1-TE-B1-1.3.1-1.2016

EUREKA
MATH

Name _____     Date _____

1. Draw place value disks on the place value chart to solve. Show each step using the standard algorithm.

   a.   4.236 ÷ 3 = _____

| Ones | Tenths | Hundredths | Thousandths |
|------|--------|------------|-------------|
|      |        |            |             |
|      |        |            |             |
|      |        |            |             |
|      |        |            |             |

$$3\overline{)4.236}$$

   b.   1.324 ÷ 2 = _____

| Ones | Tenths | Hundredths | Thousandths |
|------|--------|------------|-------------|
|      |        |            |             |
|      |        |            |             |
|      |        |            |             |

$$2\overline{)1.324}$$

**EUREKA MATH**    Lesson 14:   Divide decimals with a remainder using place value understanding and relate to a written method.    **211**

© 2015 Great Minds. eureka-math.org
G5-M1-TE-B1-1.3.1-1.2016

2. Solve using the standard algorithm.

| a.  0.78 ÷ 3 = _____ | b.  7.28 ÷ 4 = _____ | c.  17.45 ÷ 5 = _____ |
| --- | --- | --- |
| | | |

3. Grayson wrote 1.47 ÷ 7 = 2.1 in her math journal.

   Use words, numbers, or pictures to explain why Grayson's thinking is incorrect.

4. Mrs. Nguyen used 1.48 meters of netting to make 4 identical mini hockey goals. How much netting did she use per goal?

5. Esperanza usually buys avocados for $0.94 apiece. During a sale, she gets 5 avocados for $4.10. How much money did she save per avocado? Use a tape diagram, and show your calculations.

Lesson 14:  Divide decimals with a remainder using place value understanding and relate to a written method.

© 2015 Great Minds. eureka-math.org
G5-M1-TE-B1-1.3.1-1.2016

EUREKA MATH

Name _____ Date _____

1. Draw place value disks on the place value chart to solve. Show each step using the standard algorithm.

   5.372 ÷ 2 = _____

   | Ones | Tenths | Hundredths | Thousandths |
   |------|--------|------------|-------------|
   |      |        |            |             |

   $$2\overline{)5.372}$$

2. Solve using the standard algorithm.

   0.576 ÷ 4 = _____

EUREKA MATH

Lesson 14:     Divide decimals with a remainder using place value understanding
              and relate to a written method.

213

© 2015 Great Minds. eureka-math.org
G5-M1-TE-B1-1.3.1-1.2016

Name _____    Date _____

1. Draw place value disks on the place value chart to solve. Show each step using the standard algorithm.

   a.   5.241 ÷ 3 = _____

   | Ones | Tenths | Hundredths | Thousandths |
   |------|--------|------------|-------------|
   |      |        |            |             |
   |      |        |            |             |
   |      |        |            |             |
   |      |        |            |             |

   $3\overline{)5.241}$

   b.   5.372 ÷ 4 = _____

   | Ones | Tenths | Hundredths | Thousandths |
   |------|--------|------------|-------------|
   |      |        |            |             |
   |      |        |            |             |
   |      |        |            |             |
   |      |        |            |             |

   $4\overline{)5.372}$

Lesson 14:    Divide decimals with a remainder using place value understanding and relate to a written method.

© 2015 Great Minds. eureka-math.org
G5-M1-TE-B1-1.3.1-1.2016

EUREKA MATH

2. Solve using the standard algorithm.

| a.  $0.64 \div 4 =$ _____ | b.  $6.45 \div 5 =$ _____ | c.  $16.404 \div 6 =$ _____ |
|---|---|---|
| | | |

3. Mrs. Mayuko paid $40.68 for 3 kg of shrimp. What's the cost of 1 kilogram of shrimp?

4. The total weight of 6 pieces of butter and a bag of sugar is 3.8 lb. If the weight of the bag of sugar is 1.4 lb, what is the weight of each piece of butter?

Lesson 14:  Divide decimals with a remainder using place value understanding and relate to a written method.

215

© 2015 Great Minds. eureka-math.org
G5-M1-TE-B1-1.3.1-1.2016

# Lesson 15

Objective:  Divide decimals using place value understanding, including remainders in the smallest unit.

## Suggested Lesson Structure

■ Fluency Practice          (12 minutes)
■ Application Problem        (8 minutes)
■ Concept Development        (30 minutes)
■ Student Debrief           (10 minutes)
   **Total Time**           **(60 minutes)**

## Fluency Practice  (12 minutes)

- Sprint:  Multiply by Exponents  **5.NBT.2**       (8 minutes)
- Find the Quotient  **5.NBT.7**                    (4 minutes)

### Sprint:  Multiply by Exponents  (8 minutes)

Materials:    (S) Multiply by Exponents Sprint

Note:  This Sprint helps students build automaticity in multiplying decimals by $10^1$, $10^2$, $10^3$, and $10^4$.

### Find the Quotient  (4 minutes)

Materials:    (S) Millions to thousandths place value chart (Lesson 1 Template 2), personal white board

Note:  This review fluency drill helps students work toward mastery of dividing decimals using concepts introduced in Lesson 14.

    T:    (Project the place value chart showing ones, tenths, and hundredths. Write 0.48 ÷ 2 = \_\_\_.) On your place value chart, draw 48 hundredths using place value disks. (Allow students time to draw.)

    T:    (Write 48 hundredths ÷ 2 = \_\_ hundredths = \_\_ tenths \_\_ hundredths.) Solve the division problem.

    S:    (Write 48 hundredths ÷ 2 = 24 hundredths = 2 tenths 4 hundredths.)

    T:    Solve using the standard algorithm.

Repeat the process for 0.42 ÷ 3, 3.52 ÷ 2, and 96 tenths ÷ 8.

Lesson 15:      Divide decimals using place value understanding, including remainders
                                  in the smallest unit.

© 2015 Great Minds. eureka-math.org
G5-M1-TE-B1-1.3.1-1.2016

## Application Problem  (8 minutes)

Jose bought a bag of 6 oranges for $2.82. He also bought
5 pineapples. He gave the cashier $20 and received $1.43
change. How much did each pineapple cost?

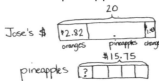

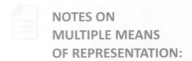

NOTES ON
MULTIPLE MEANS
OF REPRESENTATION:

Tape diagrams are a form of modeling
that offers students a way to organize,
prioritize, and contextualize
information in story problems.
Students create pictures, represented
in bars, from the words in the story
problems. Once bars are drawn and
the unknown identified, students can
find viable solutions.

Note:  This multi-step problem requires several skills taught in this module, such as multiplying decimal
numbers by single-digit whole numbers, subtraction of decimal numbers, and division of decimal numbers.
Working with these three operations helps activate prior knowledge and helps scaffold today's lesson on
decimal division. Labeling the tape diagram as a class may be a beneficial scaffold for some learners.

## Concept Development  (30 minutes)

Materials:    (S) Hundreds to thousandths place value chart (Lesson 7 Template), personal white board

**Problems 1–2**

$1.7 \div 2$

$2.6 \div 4$

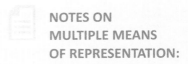

NOTES ON
MULTIPLE MEANS
OF REPRESENTATION:

T:   (Write $1.7 \div 2$ on the board, and draw a place value
chart.) Show 1.7 on your place value chart by drawing
place value disks.

For this problem, students are only using the place value chart
and drawing the place value disks. However, the teacher should
record the standard algorithm and draw the place value disks as
each unit is decomposed and shared.

In this lesson, students will need to
know that a number can be written in
multiple ways. In order to activate prior
knowledge and heighten interest,
the teacher may display a dollar bill
while writing $1 on the board. The
class could discuss that, in order for the
dollar to be divided between two
people, it must be thought of as tenths:
($1.0). Additionally, if the dollar were
to be divided by more than 10 people,
it would be thought of as hundredths:
$1.00. If students need additional
support, this could be demonstrated
using concrete materials.

T:   Let's begin with our largest unit. Can 1 one be divided
into 2 groups?

S:   No.

T:   Each group gets how many ones?

S:   0 ones.

Lesson 15:        Divide decimals using place value understanding, including remainders       **217**
                  in the smallest unit.

© 2015 Great Minds. eureka-math.org
G5-M1-TE-B1-1.3.1-1.2016

T:   (Record 0 in the ones place of the quotient in the algorithm.) We need to keep sharing. How can we share this single ones disk?

S:   Unbundle it or exchange it for 10 tenths.

T:   Draw that unbundling, and tell me how many tenths we have now.

S:   17 tenths.

T:   17 tenths divided by 2. How many tenths can we put in each group?

S:   8 tenths.

T:   Cross them off as you divide them into 2 equal groups.

S:   (Cross out tenths and share them in 2 groups.)

T:   (Record 8 tenths in the quotient in the algorithm.) How many tenths did we share in all?

S:   16 tenths.

T:   (Record 16 tenths in the algorithm.) Explain to your partner why we are subtracting the 16 tenths.

S:   (Discuss.)

T:   How many tenths are left?

S:   1 tenth.

T:   (Record the subtraction in the algorithm.) Is there a way for us to keep sharing? Turn and talk.

S:   We can make 10 hundredths with 1 tenth. → Yes. 1 tenth is still equal to 10 hundredths, even though there is no digit in the hundredths place in 1.7. → We can think about 1 and 7 tenths as 1 and 70 hundredths. They are equal.

T:   Unbundle the 1 tenth to make 10 hundredths.

S:   (Unbundle and draw.)

T:   Have you changed the value of what we needed to share? Explain.

S:   No. It's the same amount to share, but we are using smaller units. → The value is the same. 1 tenth is the same as 10 hundredths.

T:   I can show this by placing a zero in the hundredths place. (Record the 0 in the hundredths place of the algorithm. 1 tenth becomes 10 hundredths.)

T:   Now that we have 10 hundredths, can we divide this between our 2 groups? How many hundredths are in each group?

S:   Yes. 5 hundredths are in each group.

T:   Let's cross them off as you divide them into 2 equal groups.

S:   (Work.)

T:   (Record 5 hundredths in the quotient in the algorithm.) How many hundredths did we share in all?

S:   10 hundredths.

T:   (Record 10 hundredths in the algorithm.) How many hundredths are left?

S:   0 hundredths.

T:   (Record the subtraction in the algorithm.) Do we have any other units that we need to share?

S:   No.

Lesson 15:     Divide decimals using place value understanding, including remainders
                             in the smallest unit.                                          EUREKA
                                                                                           MATH

T:   Tell me the quotient in unit form and then in standard form.

S:   0 ones 8 tenths 5 hundredths: 85 hundredths. 0.85.

T:   (Show 6.72 ÷ 3 = 2.24 recorded in the standard algorithm and 1.7 ÷ 2 = 0.85 recorded in the standard algorithm side by side.) Compare these two problems. How do they differ? Turn and share with your partner.

S:   One equation has a divisor of 3, and the other equation has a divisor of 2. → Both quotients have 2 decimal places. 6.72 has digits in the tenths and hundredths, and 1.7 only has a digit in the tenths. → In order to divide 1.7, we have to think about our dividend as 1 and 70 hundredths to keep sharing.

T:   That's right! In today's problem, we had to record a zero in the hundredths place to show how we unbundled. Did recording that zero change the amount that we had to share—1 and 7 tenths? Why or why not?

S:   No, because 1 and 70 hundredths is the same amount as 1 and 7 tenths.

For the next problem (2.6 ÷ 4), repeat this sequence. Model the process on the place value chart while students record the steps of the algorithm. Stop along the way to make connections between the concrete materials and the written method.

## Problems 3–4

17 ÷ 4

22 ÷ 8

T:   (Write 17 ÷ 4 on the board.) Look at this expression. What do you notice? Turn and share with your partner.

S:   When we divide 17 into 4 groups, we have a remainder.

T:   In fourth grade, we recorded this remainder as R1. What have we done today that lets us keep sharing this remainder?

S:   We can unbundle the ones into tenths or hundredths and continue to divide.

T:   With your partner, use the place value chart to solve this problem. Partner A will draw the place value disks, and Partner B will solve using the standard algorithm.

S:   (Solve.)

T:   Compare your work. Match each number in the algorithm with its counterpart in the drawing.

Circulate to ensure that students are using their whole-number experiences with division to share decimal units. Check for misconceptions in recording. For the second problem in the set, partners should switch roles.

## Problem 5

7.7 ÷ 4

T:   (Write 7.7 ÷ 4 = _____ on the board.) Solve independently, using the standard algorithm.

S:   (Solve.)

T:   Compare your answer with your partner's.

**Problem 6**

0.84 ÷ 4

    T:   (Write 0.84 ÷ 4 = _____ on the board.) Solve independently, using the standard algorithm.

    S:   (Solve.)

    T:   Compare your answer with your neighbor's.

## Problem Set  (10 minutes)

Students should do their personal best to complete the Problem Set within the allotted 10 minutes. For some classes, it may be appropriate to modify the assignment by specifying which problems they work on first. Some problems do not specify a method for solving. Students should solve these problems using the RDW approach used for Application Problems.

## Student Debrief  (10 minutes)

**Lesson Objective:**  Divide decimals using place value understanding, including remainders in the smallest unit.

The Student Debrief is intended to invite reflection and active processing of the total lesson experience.

Invite students to review their solutions for the Problem Set. They should check work by comparing answers with a partner before going over answers as a class. Look for misconceptions or misunderstandings that can be addressed in the Debrief. Guide students in a conversation to debrief the Problem Set and process the lesson.

Any combination of the questions below may be used to lead the discussion.

- In Problems 1(a) and 1(b), which division strategy did you find more efficient—drawing place value disks or using the algorithm?

- How are Problems 2(c) and 2(f) different from the others? Will a whole number divided by a whole number always result in a whole number?

- Explain why these problems resulted in a decimal quotient.

- Take out the Problem Set from Lesson 14. Compare and contrast the first page of each assignment. Talk about what you notice.

- Take a look at Problem 2(f). What was different about how you solved this problem?

- When you solved Problem 4, what did you notice about the units used to measure the juice? (Students may not have recognized that the orange juice was measured in milliliters.) How do we proceed if we have unlike units?

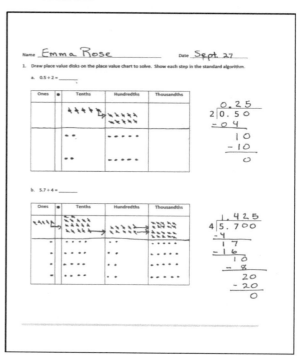

**Lesson 15:**    Divide decimals using place value understanding, including remainders in the smallest unit.

© 2015 Great Minds. eureka-math.org
G5-M1-TE-B1-1.3.1-1.2016

## Exit Ticket  (3 minutes)

After the Student Debrief, instruct students to complete the Exit Ticket. A review of their work will help with assessing students' understanding of the concepts that were presented in today's lesson and planning more effectively for future lessons. The questions may be read aloud to the students.

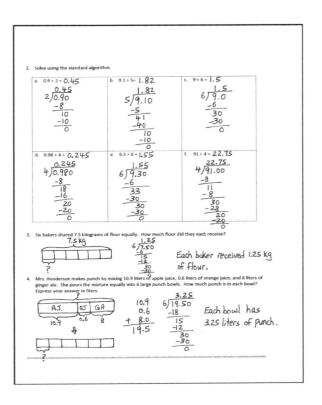

          **Lesson 15:**     Divide decimals using place value understanding, including remainders          **221**
in the smallest unit.

© 2015 Great Minds. eureka-math.org
G5-M1-TE-B1-1.3.1-1.2016

# A

Number Correct: _____

Multiply by Exponents

| | | |
|---|---|---|
| 1. | $10 \times 10 =$ | |
| 2. | $10^2 =$ | |
| 3. | $10^2 \times 10 =$ | |
| 4. | $10^3 =$ | |
| 5. | $10^3 \times 10 =$ | |
| 6. | $10^4 =$ | |
| 7. | $3 \times 100 =$ | |
| 8. | $3 \times 10^2 =$ | |
| 9. | $3.1 \times 10^2 =$ | |
| 10. | $3.15 \times 10^2 =$ | |
| 11. | $3.157 \times 10^2 =$ | |
| 12. | $4 \times 1,000 =$ | |
| 13. | $4 \times 10^3 =$ | |
| 14. | $4.2 \times 10^3 =$ | |
| 15. | $4.28 \times 10^3 =$ | |
| 16. | $4.283 \times 10^3 =$ | |
| 17. | $5 \times 10,000 =$ | |
| 18. | $5 \times 10^4 =$ | |
| 19. | $5.7 \times 10^4 =$ | |
| 20. | $5.73 \times 10^4 =$ | |
| 21. | $5.731 \times 10^4 =$ | |
| 22. | $24 \times 100 =$ | |

| | | |
|---|---|---|
| 23. | $24 \times 10^2 =$ | |
| 24. | $24.7 \times 10^2 =$ | |
| 25. | $24.07 \times 10^2 =$ | |
| 26. | $24.007 \times 10^2 =$ | |
| 27. | $53 \times 1,000 =$ | |
| 28. | $53 \times 10^3 =$ | |
| 29. | $53.8 \times 10^3 =$ | |
| 30. | $53.08 \times 10^3 =$ | |
| 31. | $53.082 \times 10^3 =$ | |
| 32. | $9.1 \times 10,000 =$ | |
| 33. | $9.1 \times 10^4 =$ | |
| 34. | $91.4 \times 10^4 =$ | |
| 35. | $91.104 \times 10^4 =$ | |
| 36. | $91.107 \times 10^4 =$ | |
| 37. | $1.2 \times 10^2 =$ | |
| 38. | $0.35 \times 10^3 =$ | |
| 39. | $5.492 \times 10^4 =$ | |
| 40. | $8.04 \times 10^3 =$ | |
| 41. | $7.109 \times 10^4 =$ | |
| 42. | $0.058 \times 10^2 =$ | |
| 43. | $20.78 \times 10^3 =$ | |
| 44. | $420.079 \times 10^2 =$ | |

Lesson 15: Divide decimals using place value understanding, including remainders in the smallest unit.

© 2015 Great Minds. eureka-math.org
G5-M1-TE-B1-1.3.1-1.2016

EUREKA MATH

# B

Number Correct: _____

Improvement: _____

Multiply by Exponents

| | | |
|---|---|---|
| 1. | $10 \times 10 \times 1 =$ | |
| 2. | $10^2 =$ | |
| 3. | $10^2 \times 10 =$ | |
| 4. | $10^3 =$ | |
| 5. | $10^3 \times 10 =$ | |
| 6. | $10^4 =$ | |
| 7. | $4 \times 100 =$ | |
| 8. | $4 \times 10^2 =$ | |
| 9. | $4.1 \times 10^2 =$ | |
| 10. | $4.15 \times 10^2 =$ | |
| 11. | $4.157 \times 10^2 =$ | |
| 12. | $5 \times 1,000 =$ | |
| 13. | $5 \times 10^3 =$ | |
| 14. | $5.2 \times 10^3 =$ | |
| 15. | $5.28 \times 10^3 =$ | |
| 16. | $5.283 \times 10^3 =$ | |
| 17. | $7 \times 10,000 =$ | |
| 18. | $7 \times 10^4 =$ | |
| 19. | $7.5 \times 10^4 =$ | |
| 20. | $7.53 \times 10^4 =$ | |
| 21. | $7.531 \times 10^4 =$ | |
| 22. | $42 \times 100 =$ | |

| | | |
|---|---|---|
| 23. | $42 \times 10^2 =$ | |
| 24. | $42.7 \times 10^2 =$ | |
| 25. | $42.07 \times 10^2 =$ | |
| 26. | $42.007 \times 10^2 =$ | |
| 27. | $35 \times 1,000 =$ | |
| 28. | $35 \times 10^3 =$ | |
| 29. | $35.8 \times 10^3 =$ | |
| 30. | $35.08 \times 10^3 =$ | |
| 31. | $35.082 \times 10^3 =$ | |
| 32. | $8.1 \times 10,000 =$ | |
| 33. | $8.1 \times 10^4 =$ | |
| 34. | $81.4 \times 10^4 =$ | |
| 35. | $81.104 \times 10^4 =$ | |
| 36. | $81.107 \times 10^4 =$ | |
| 37. | $1.3 \times 10^2 =$ | |
| 38. | $0.53 \times 10^3 =$ | |
| 39. | $4.391 \times 10^4 =$ | |
| 40. | $7.03 \times 10^3 =$ | |
| 41. | $6.109 \times 10^4 =$ | |
| 42. | $0.085 \times 10^2 =$ | |
| 43. | $30.87 \times 10^3 =$ | |
| 44. | $530.097 \times 10^2 =$ | |

Lesson 15:    Divide decimals using place value understanding, including remainders in the smallest unit.

223

Name _____  Date _____

1. Draw place value disks on the place value chart to solve. Show each step in the standard algorithm.

   a.  0.5 ÷ 2 = _____

   | Ones | • | Tenths | Hundredths | Thousandths |
   |------|---|--------|------------|-------------|
   |      |   |        |            |             |

   ```
   2 | 0 . 5
   ```

   b.  5.7 ÷ 4 = _____

   | Ones | • | Tenths | Hundredths | Thousandths |
   |------|---|--------|------------|-------------|
   |      |   |        |            |             |

   ```
   4 | 5 . 7
   ```

Lesson 15:      Divide decimals using place value understanding, including remainders in the smallest unit.

© 2015 Great Minds. eureka-math.org
G5-M1-TE-B1-1.3.1-1.2016

EUREKA MATH

2. Solve using the standard algorithm.

| | | |
|---|---|---|
| a. $0.9 \div 2 =$ | b. $9.1 \div 5 =$ | c. $9 \div 6 =$ |
| d. $0.98 \div 4 =$ | e. $9.3 \div 6 =$ | f. $91 \div 4 =$ |

3. Six bakers shared 7.5 kilograms of flour equally. How much flour did they each receive?

4. Mrs. Henderson makes punch by mixing 10.9 liters of apple juice, 0.6 liters of orange juice, and 8 liters of ginger ale. She pours the mixture equally into 6 large punch bowls. How much punch is in each bowl? Express your answer in liters.

EUREKA MATH

Lesson 15: Divide decimals using place value understanding, including remainders in the smallest unit.

225

© 2015 Great Minds. eureka-math.org
G5-M1-TE-B1-1.3.1-1.2016

Name _____ Date _____

1. Draw place value disks on the place value chart to solve. Show each step in the standard algorithm.

   0.9 ÷ 4 = _____

   | Ones | • | Tenths | Hundredths | Thousandths |
   |------|---|--------|------------|-------------|
   |      |   |        |            |             |

   $4\overline{)0.9}$

2. Solve using the standard algorithm.

   9.8 ÷ 5 =

**Lesson 15:** Divide decimals using place value understanding, including remainders in the smallest unit.

Name _____     Date _____

1. Draw place value disks on the place value chart to solve. Show each step in the standard algorithm.

    a.   0.7 ÷ 4 = _____

| Ones | • | Tenths | Hundredths | Thousandths |
|------|---|--------|------------|-------------|
|      |   |        |            |             |

$4\overline{\smash{)}0.7}$

    b.   8.1 ÷ 5 = _____

| Ones | • | Tenths | Hundredths | Thousandths |
|------|---|--------|------------|-------------|
|      |   |        |            |             |

$5\overline{\smash{)}8.1}$

2. Solve using the standard algorithm.

| a. $0.7 \div 2 =$ | b. $3.9 \div 6 =$ | c. $9 \div 4 =$ |
|---|---|---|
| d. $0.92 \div 2 =$ | e. $9.4 \div 4 =$ | f. $91 \div 8 =$ |

3. A rope 8.7 meters long is cut into 5 equal pieces. How long is each piece?

4. Yasmine bought 6 gallons of apple juice. After filling up 4 bottles of the same size with apple juice, she had 0.3 gallon of apple juice left. How many gallons of apple juice are in each container?

Lesson 15:    Divide decimals using place value understanding, including remainders in the smallest unit.

© 2015 Great Minds. eureka-math.org
G5-M1-TE-B1-1.3.1-1.2016

EUREKA MATH

# Lesson 16

Objective:  Solve word problems using decimal operations.

## Suggested Lesson Structure

■ Fluency Practice     (12 minutes)
■ Application Problem     (7 minutes)
■ Concept Development     (31 minutes)
■ Student Debrief     (10 minutes)
    **Total Time**     **(60 minutes)**

## Fluency Practice  (12 minutes)

- Sprint:  Multiply and Divide by Exponents  **5.NBT.2**     (8 minutes)
- Find the Quotient  **5.NBT.7**     (4 minutes)

### Sprint:  Multiply and Divide by Exponents  (8 minutes)

Materials:  (S) Multiply and Divide by Exponents Sprint

Note:  This Sprint helps students build automaticity in dividing decimals by $10^1$, $10^2$, $10^3$, and $10^4$.

### Find the Quotient  (4 minutes)

Materials:  (S) Hundreds through thousandths place value chart (Lesson 7 Template), personal white board

Note:  This review fluency drill helps students work toward mastery of dividing decimals using concepts introduced in Lesson 15.

    T:     (Project the place value chart showing ones, tenths, and hundredths. Write 0.3 ÷ 2 = ___.) Use place value disks to draw 3 tenths on your place value chart. (Allow students time to draw.)
    T:     (Write 3 tenths ÷ 2 = ___ hundredths ÷ 2 = ___ tenths ___ hundredths on the board.) Solve the division problem.
    S:     (Write 3 tenths ÷ 2 = 30 hundredths ÷ 2 = 1 tenth 5 hundredths.)
    T:     (Write the algorithm below 3 tenths ÷ 2 = 30 hundredths ÷ 2 = 1 tenth 5 hundredths.) Solve using the standard algorithm. (Allow students time to solve.)

Repeat the process for 0.9 ÷ 5, 6.7 ÷ 5, 0.58 ÷ 4, and 93 tenths ÷ 6.

## Application Problem  (7 minutes)

Jesse and three friends buy snacks for a hike. They buy trail mix for $5.42, apples for $2.55, and granola bars for $3.39. If the four friends split the cost of the snacks equally, how much should each friend pay?

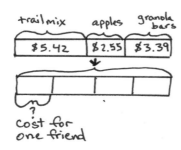

Note:  Adding and dividing decimals are taught in this module. Teachers may choose to help students draw the tape diagram before students do the calculations independently.

## Concept Development  (31 minutes)

Materials:    (T/S) Problem Set, pencil

### Problem 1

Mr. Frye distributed $126 equally among his 4 children for their weekly allowance. How much money did each child receive?

As the teacher creates each component of the tape diagram, students should re-create the tape diagram on their Problem Sets.

T:   We will solve Problem 1 on the Problem Set together. (Project the problem on the board.) Read the word problem together.

S:   (Read chorally.)

T:   Who and what is this problem about? Let's identify our variables.

S:   Mr. Frye's money.

T:   Draw a bar to represent Mr. Frye's money. (Draw a rectangle on the board.)

*Mr. Frye's Money*      [ rectangle ]

T:   Let's read the problem sentence by sentence and adjust our diagram to match the information in the problem. Read the first sentence together.

S:   (Read.)

T:   What is the important information in the first sentence? Turn and talk.

S:   $126 and 4 children received an equal amount.

Lesson 16:       Solve word problems using decimal operations.

EUREKA
MATH

T:   (Underline the stated information.) How can I represent this information in my diagram?

S:   126 dollars is the total, so put a bracket on top of the bar, and label it.

T:   (Draw a bracket over the diagram and label as $126. Have students label their diagrams.)

T:   How many children share the 126 dollars?

S:   4 children.

T:   How can we represent this information?

S:   Divide the bar into 4 equal parts.

T:   (Partition the diagram into 4 equal sections, and have students do the same.)

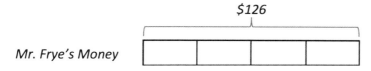

**NOTES ON MULTIPLE MEANS OF REPRESENTATION:**

Students may use various approaches for calculating the quotient. Some may use place value units 12 tens + 60 tenths. Others may use the division algorithm. Comparing computation strategies may help students develop their mathematical thinking.

T:   What is the question?

S:   How much did each child receive?

T:   What is unknown in this problem? How will we represent it in our diagram?

S:   The amount of money one of Mr. Frye's children received for allowance is what we are trying to find. We should put a question mark inside one of the parts.

T:   (Write a question mark inside one section of the tape diagram.)

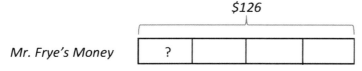

**NOTES ON MULTIPLE MEANS OF ENGAGEMENT:**

If students struggle to draw a model of word problems involving division with decimal values, scaffold their understanding by modeling an analogous problem substituting simpler, whole-number values. Then, using the same tape diagram, erase the whole-number values, and replace them with the parallel values from the decimal problem.

T:   Make a unit statement about your diagram. How many unit bars are equal to $126?

S:   Four units is the same as $126.

T:   How can we find the value of one unit?

S:   Divide $126 by 4. → Use division because we have a whole that we are sharing equally.

T:   What is the expression that will give us the amount that each child received?

S:   $126 ÷ 4.

T: Solve and express your answer in a complete sentence.

$126

Mr. Frye's Money

| ? | | | |
|---|---|---|---|

4 units = $126
1 unit  = ?
1 unit  = $126 ÷ 4
         = $31.50

S: Each child received $31.50 for his weekly allowance.
T: Read Part (b) of Problem 1, and solve using a tape diagram.
S: (Work for 5 minutes.)

As students are working, circulate and be attentive to accuracy and labeling of information in the students' tape diagrams. Refer to the example student work on the Problem Set for one example of an accurate tape diagram.

## Problem 4

Brandon mixed 6.83 lb of cashews with 3.57 lb of pistachios. After filling up 6 bags that were the same size with the mixture, he had 0.35 lb of nuts left. What was the weight of each bag?

T: (Project Problem 4.) Read the problem. Identify the variables (who and what), and draw a bar.
S: (Read and draw. Draw a bar on the board.)

Brandon's Cashews and Pistachios

T: Read the first sentence.
S: (Read.)
T: What is the important information in this sentence? Tell a partner.
S: 6.83 lb of cashews and 3.57 lb of pistachios.
T: (Underline the stated information.) How can I represent this information in the tape diagram?

**MP.8**

S: Show two parts inside the bar.
T: Should the parts be equal in size?
S: No. The cashews part should be about twice the size of the pistachios part.

6.83                    3.57

Brandon's Cashews/Pistachios

Lesson 16:    Solve word problems using decimal operations.

EUREKA MATH

T:   (Draw and label.) Let's read the next sentence. How will we represent this part of the problem?

S:   We could draw another bar to represent both kinds of nuts together. Then, split the bar into parts to show the bags and the part that was left over. → We could erase the bar separating the nuts, put the total on the bar we already drew, and split it into the equal parts. We would have to remember he had some nuts left over.

T:   Both are good ideas. Choose one for your model. I am going to use the bar that I've already drawn. I'll label my bags with the letter *b*, and I'll label the part that wasn't put into a bag.

T:   (Erase the bar between the types of nuts. Draw a bracket over the bar, and write the total. Show the leftover nuts and the 6 bags.)

*Brandon's Cashews/Pistachios*

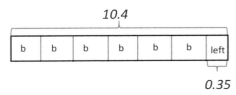

T:   What is the question?

S:   How much did each bag weigh?

T:   Where should we put our question mark?

S:   Inside one of the units that is labeled with the letter *b*.

*Brandon's Cashews/Pistachios*

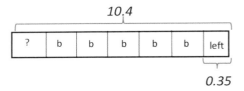

T:   How will we find the value of 1 unit in our diagram? Turn and talk.

S:   Part of the weight is being placed into 6 bags, so we need to divide that part by 6. → There was a part that didn't get put in a bag. We have to take the leftover part away from the total so we can find the part that was divided into the bags. Then, we can divide.

T:   Perform your calculations, and state your answer in a complete sentence. (See the solution on the next page.)

### NOTES ON MULTIPLE MEANS OF REPRESENTATION:

Complex relationships within a tape diagram can be made clearer to students with the use of color. The bags of cashews in Problem 4 could be made more visible by outlining the bagged nuts in red. This creates a classic part–part–whole problem. Students can readily see the portion that must be subtracted in order to produce the portion divided into 6 bags.

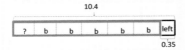

If using color to highlight relationships is still too abstract for students, colored paper can be cut, marked, and manipulated.

Thinking Blocks is a free Internet site that offers students with fine motor deficits a tool for drawing bars and labels electronically. Models can be printed for sharing with classmates.

*Brandon's Cashews/Pistachios*

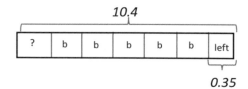

6 units + 0.35 = 10.4

1 unit = (10.4 − 0.35) ÷ 6

1 unit = 1.675 lb

Each bag contained 1.675 lb of nuts.

T:   Complete Problems 2, 3, and 5 on the Problem Set, using a tape diagram and calculations to solve.

Circulate as students work. Listen for sound mathematical reasoning.

## Problem Set  (10 minutes)

Today's Problem Set forms the basis of the Concept Development. Students solve Problems 1 and 4 with teacher guidance, modeling, and scaffolding. Problems 2, 3, and 5 are designed to be independent work.

## Student Debrief  (10 minutes)

**Lesson Objective:**  Solve word problems using decimal operations.

The Student Debrief is intended to invite reflection and active processing of the total lesson experience.

Invite students to review their solutions for the Problem Set. They should check work by comparing answers with a partner before going over answers as a class. Look for misconceptions or misunderstandings that can be addressed in the Debrief. Guide students in a conversation to debrief the Problem Set and process the lesson.

**NOTES ON MULTIPLE MEANS OF REPRESENTATION:**

The equations pictured to the left are a formal teacher solution for Problem 4. Students should not be expected to produce such a formal representation of their thinking. Students are more likely to simply show a vertical subtraction of the leftover nuts from the total and then show a division of the bagged nuts into 6 equal portions. There may be other appropriate strategies for solving offered by students as well.

Teacher solutions offer an opportunity to expose students to more formal representations. These solutions might be written on the board as a way to translate a student's approach to solving as the student communicates the strategy aloud to the class.

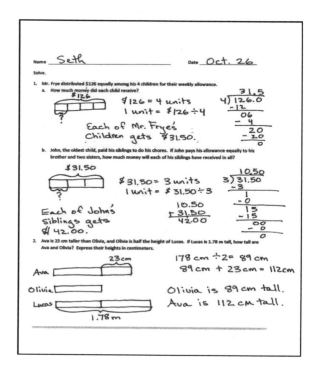

Lesson 16:      Solve word problems using decimal operations.

**EUREKA MATH**

Any combination of the questions below may be used to lead the discussion.

- How did the tape diagram in Problem 1(a) help you solve Problem 1(b)?

- In Problem 3, how did you represent the information using the tape diagram?

- Look at Problem 1(b) and Problem 5(b). How are the questions different? (Problem 1(b) is partitive division—groups are known, size of group is unknown. Problem 5(b) is measurement division—size of group is known, number of groups is unknown.) Does the difference in the questions affect the calculation of the answers?

- As an extension or an option for early finishers, have students generate word problems based on labeled tape diagrams, or have them create one of each type of division problem (group size unknown and number of groups unknown).

## Exit Ticket  (3 minutes)

After the Student Debrief, instruct students to complete the Exit Ticket. A review of their work will help with assessing students' understanding of the concepts that were presented in today's lesson and planning more effectively for future lessons. The questions may be read aloud to the students.

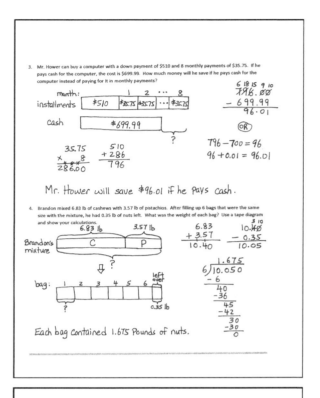

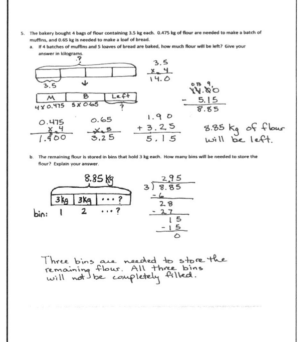

# A

Number Correct: _____

Multiply and Divide by Exponents

| | | |
|---|---|---|
| 1. | $10 \times 10 =$ | |
| 2. | $10^2 =$ | |
| 3. | $10^2 \times 10 =$ | |
| 4. | $10^3 =$ | |
| 5. | $10^3 \times 10 =$ | |
| 6. | $10^4 =$ | |
| 7. | $3 \times 100 =$ | |
| 8. | $3 \times 10^2 =$ | |
| 9. | $3.1 \times 10^2 =$ | |
| 10. | $3.15 \times 10^2 =$ | |
| 11. | $3.157 \times 10^2 =$ | |
| 12. | $4 \times 1,000 =$ | |
| 13. | $4 \times 10^3 =$ | |
| 14. | $4.2 \times 10^3 =$ | |
| 15. | $4.28 \times 10^3 =$ | |
| 16. | $4.283 \times 10^3 =$ | |
| 17. | $5 \times 10,000 =$ | |
| 18. | $5 \times 10^4 =$ | |
| 19. | $5.7 \times 10^4 =$ | |
| 20. | $5.73 \times 10^4 =$ | |
| 21. | $5.731 \times 10^4 =$ | |
| 22. | $24 \times 100 =$ | |

| | | |
|---|---|---|
| 23. | $3,400 \div 10^2 =$ | |
| 24. | $3,470 \div 10^2 =$ | |
| 25. | $3,407 \div 10^2 =$ | |
| 26. | $3,400.7 \div 10^2 =$ | |
| 27. | $63,000 \div 1,000 =$ | |
| 28. | $63,000 \div 10^3 =$ | |
| 29. | $63,800 \div 10^3 =$ | |
| 30. | $63,080 \div 10^3 =$ | |
| 31. | $63,082 \div 10^3 =$ | |
| 32. | $81,000 \div 10,000 =$ | |
| 33. | $81,000 \div 10^4 =$ | |
| 34. | $81,400 \div 10^4 =$ | |
| 35. | $81,040 \div 10^4 =$ | |
| 36. | $91,070 \div 10^4 =$ | |
| 37. | $120 \div 10^2 =$ | |
| 38. | $350 \div 10^3 =$ | |
| 39. | $45,920 \div 10^4 =$ | |
| 40. | $6,040 \div 10^3 =$ | |
| 41. | $61,080 \div 10^4 =$ | |
| 42. | $7.8 \div 10^2 =$ | |
| 43. | $40,870 \div 10^3 =$ | |
| 44. | $52,070.9 \div 10^2 =$ | |

Lesson 16:     Solve word problems using decimal operations.

EUREKA MATH

# B

Number Correct: _____

Improvement: _____

Multiply and Divide by Exponents

| | | |
|---|---|---|
| 1. | $10 \times 10 \times 1 =$ | |
| 2. | $10^2 =$ | |
| 3. | $10^2 \times 10 =$ | |
| 4. | $10^3 =$ | |
| 5. | $10^3 \times 10 =$ | |
| 6. | $10^4 =$ | |
| 7. | $500 \div 100 =$ | |
| 8. | $500 \div 10^2 =$ | |
| 9. | $510 \div 10^2 =$ | |
| 10. | $516 \div 10^2 =$ | |
| 11. | $516.7 \div 10^2 =$ | |
| 12. | $6,000 \div 1,000 =$ | |
| 13. | $6,000 \div 10^3 =$ | |
| 14. | $6,200 \div 10^3 =$ | |
| 15. | $6,280 \div 10^3 =$ | |
| 16. | $6,283 \div 10^3 =$ | |
| 17. | $70,000 \div 10,000 =$ | |
| 18. | $70,000 \div 10^4 =$ | |
| 19. | $76,000 \div 10^4 =$ | |
| 20. | $76,300 \div 10^4 =$ | |
| 21. | $76,310 \div 10^4 =$ | |
| 22. | $4,300 \div 100 =$ | |

| | | |
|---|---|---|
| 23. | $4,300 \div 10^2 =$ | |
| 24. | $4,370 \div 10^2 =$ | |
| 25. | $4,307 \div 10^2 =$ | |
| 26. | $4,300.7 \div 10^2 =$ | |
| 27. | $73,000 \div 1,000 =$ | |
| 28. | $73,000 \div 10^3 =$ | |
| 29. | $73,800 \div 10^3 =$ | |
| 30. | $73,080 \div 10^3 =$ | |
| 31. | $73,082 \div 10^3 =$ | |
| 32. | $91,000 \div 10,000 =$ | |
| 33. | $91,000 \div 10^4 =$ | |
| 34. | $91,400 \div 10^4 =$ | |
| 35. | $91,040 \div 10^4 =$ | |
| 36. | $81,070 \div 10^4 =$ | |
| 37. | $170 \div 10^2 =$ | |
| 38. | $450 \div 10^3 =$ | |
| 39. | $54,920 \div 10^4 =$ | |
| 40. | $4,060 \div 10^3 =$ | |
| 41. | $71,080 \div 10^4 =$ | |
| 42. | $8.7 \div 10^2 =$ | |
| 43. | $60,470 \div 10^3 =$ | |
| 44. | $72,050.9 \div 10^2 =$ | |

Lesson 16:     Solve word problems using decimal operations.

**237**

© 2015 Great Minds. eureka-math.org
G5-M1-TE-B1-1.3.1-1.2016

Name _____  Date _____

Solve.

1. Mr. Frye distributed $126 equally among his 4 children for their weekly allowance.

    a.  How much money did each child receive?

    b.  John, the oldest child, paid his siblings to do his chores. If John pays his allowance equally to his brother and two sisters, how much money will each of his siblings have received in all?

2. Ava is 23 cm taller than Olivia, and Olivia is half the height of Lucas. If Lucas is 1.78 m tall, how tall are Ava and Olivia? Express their heights in centimeters.

Lesson 16:     Solve word problems using decimal operations.

**EUREKA MATH**

© 2015 Great Minds. eureka-math.org
G5-M1-TE-B1-1.3.1-1.2016

3. Mr. Hower can buy a computer with a down payment of $510 and 8 monthly payments of $35.75. If he pays cash for the computer, the cost is $699.99. How much money will he save if he pays cash for the computer instead of paying for it in monthly payments?

4. Brandon mixed 6.83 lb of cashews with 3.57 lb of pistachios. After filling up 6 bags that were the same size with the mixture, he had 0.35 lb of nuts left. What was the weight of each bag? Use a tape diagram, and show your calculations.

5. The bakery bought 4 bags of flour containing 3.5 kg each. 0.475 kg of flour is needed to make a batch of muffins, and 0.65 kg is needed to make a loaf of bread.

   a. If 4 batches of muffins and 5 loaves of bread are baked, how much flour will be left? Give your answer in kilograms.

   b. The remaining flour is stored in bins that hold 3 kg each. How many bins will be needed to store the flour? Explain your answer.

Lesson 16:    Solve word problems using decimal operations.

© 2015 Great Minds. eureka-math.org
G5-M1-TE-B1-1.3.1-1.2016

Name _____ Date _____

Write a word problem with two questions that matches the tape diagram below, and then solve.

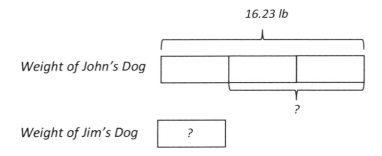

16.23 lb

Weight of John's Dog

?

Weight of Jim's Dog    ?

Name _____   Date _____

Solve using tape diagrams.

1. A gardener installed 42.6 meters of fencing in a week. He installed 13.45 meters on Monday and 9.5 meters on Tuesday. He installed the rest of the fence in equal lengths on Wednesday through Friday. How many meters of fencing did he install on each of the last three days?

2. Jenny charges $9.15 an hour to babysit toddlers and $7.45 an hour to babysit school-aged children.

   a. If Jenny babysat toddlers for 9 hours and school-aged children for 6 hours, how much money did she earn in all?

   b. Jenny wants to earn $1,300 by the end of the summer. How much more will she need to earn to meet her goal?

Lesson 16:  Solve word problems using decimal operations.

EUREKA MATH

3. A table and 8 chairs weigh 235.68 lb together. If the table weighs 157.84 lb, what is the weight of one chair in pounds?

4. Mrs. Cleaver mixes 1.24 liters of red paint with 3 times as much blue paint to make purple paint. She pours the paint equally into 5 containers. How much blue paint is in each container? Give your answer in liters.

EUREKA
MATH

Lesson 16:     Solve word problems using decimal operations.

243

© 2015 Great Minds. eureka-math.org
G5-M1-TE-B1-1.3.1-1.2016

Name _____ Date _____

1. The following equations involve different quantities and use different operations, yet produce the same result. Use a place value chart and words to explain why this is true.

$$4.13 \times 10^3 = 4130 \qquad\qquad 413{,}000 \div 10^2 = 4130$$

2. Use an area model to explain the product of 4.6 and 3. Write the product in standard form, word form, and expanded form.

EUREKA MATH

3. Compare using >, <, or =.

  a. 2 tenths + 11 hundredths          0.13

  b. 13 tenths + 8 tenths + 32 hundredths       2.42

  c. 342 hundredths + 7 tenths          3 + 49 hundredths

  d. $2 + 31 \times \frac{1}{10} + 14 \times \frac{1}{100}$          2.324

  e. $14 + 72 \times \frac{1}{10} + 4 \times \frac{1}{1000}$      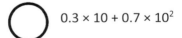    21.24

  f. $0.3 \times 10^2 + 0.007 \times 10^3$      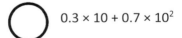    $0.3 \times 10 + 0.7 \times 10^2$

4. Dr. Mann mixed 10.357 g of chemical A, 12.062 g of chemical B, and 7.506 g of chemical C to make 5 doses of medicine.

   a. About how much medicine did he make in grams? Estimate the amount of each chemical by rounding to the nearest tenth of a gram before finding the sum. Show all your thinking.

   b. Find the actual amount of medicine mixed by Dr. Mann. What is the difference between your estimate and the actual amount?

   c. How many grams are in one dose of medicine? Explain your strategy for solving this problem.

   d. Round the weight of one dose to the nearest gram.

© 2015 Great Minds. eureka-math.org
G5-M1-TE-B1-1.3.1-1.2016

**Generalize place value understanding for multi-digit whole numbers.**

**5.NBT.1**   Recognize that in a multi-digit number, a digit in one place represents 10 times as much as it represents in the place to its right and 1/10 of what it represents in the place to its left.

**5.NBT.2.**   Explain patterns in the number of zeros of the product when multiplying a number by powers of 10, and explain patterns in the placement of the decimal point when a decimal is multiplied or divided by a power of 10. Use whole-number exponents to denote powers of 10.

**5.NBT.3**   Read, write, and compare decimals to thousandths.

    a.   Read and write decimals to thousandths using base-ten numerals, number names, and expanded form, e.g., $347.392 = 3 \times 100 + 4 \times 10 + 7 \times 1 + 3 \times (1/10) + 9 \times (1/100) + 2 \times (1/1000)$.

    b.   Compare two decimals to thousandths based on meanings of the digits in each place, using >, =, and < symbols to record the results of comparisons.

**5.NBT.4**   Use place value understanding to round decimals to any place.

**Perform operations with multi-digit whole numbers and with decimals to hundredths.**

**5.NBT.7**   Add, subtract, multiply, and divide decimals to hundredths, using concrete models or drawings and strategies based on place value, properties of operations, and/or the relationship between addition and subtraction; relate the strategy to a written method and explain the reasoning used.

**Convert like measurement units within a given measurement system.**

**5.MD.1**   Convert among different-sized standard measurement units within a given measurement system (e.g., convert 5 cm to 0.05 m), and use these conversions in solving multi-step, real world problems.

## Evaluating Student Learning Outcomes

A Progression Toward Mastery is provided to describe steps that illuminate the gradually increasing understandings that students develop on their way to proficiency. In this chart, this progress is presented from left (Step 1) to right (Step 4). The learning goal for students is to achieve Step 4 mastery. These steps are meant to help teachers and students identify and celebrate what the students CAN do now and what they need to work on next.

## A Progression Toward Mastery

| Assessment Task Item and Standards Assessed | STEP 1 Little evidence of reasoning without a correct answer. (1 Point) | STEP 2 Evidence of some reasoning without a correct answer. (2 Points) | STEP 3 Evidence of some reasoning with a correct answer or evidence of solid reasoning with an incorrect answer. (3 Points) | STEP 4 Evidence of solid reasoning with a correct answer. (4 Points) |
|---|---|---|---|---|
| 1<br><br>5.NBT.1<br>5.NBT.2 | Student is unable to provide a correct response. | Student attempts but is not able to accurately draw the place value chart or explain reasoning fully. | Student correctly draws the place value chart but does not show full reasoning or explains reasoning fully, but the place value chart does not match the reasoning. | Student correctly:<br><br>▪ Draws the place value chart showing movement of digits.<br>▪ Explains the movement of units to the left for multiplication and the movement of units to the right for division. |
| 2<br><br>5.NBT.7 | Student is unable to use the area model to find the product. | Student attempts to use an area model to multiply but does so inaccurately. Student attempts to write either the word or expanded form of an inaccurate product. | Student uses the area model to multiply but does not find the correct product. The student accurately produces a word and expanded form of an inaccurate product. | Student correctly:<br><br>▪ Draws an area model.<br>▪ Shows work to find the product of 13.8.<br>▪ Accurately expresses the product in both word and expanded form. |
| 3<br><br>5.NBT.3a<br>5.NBT.3b | Student answers none or one part correctly. | Student answers two or three answers correctly. | Student answers four or five answers correctly. | Student correctly answers all six parts.<br><br>a.  >      d.  ><br>b.  =      e.  <<br>c.  >      f.  < |

Module 1:      Place Value and Decimal Fractions

| A Progression Toward Mastery | | | | |
|---|---|---|---|---|
| **4**<br><br>**5.NBT.1**<br>**5.NBT.2**<br>**5.NBT.3a**<br>**5.NBT.3b**<br>**5.NBT.4**<br>**5.NBT.7**<br>**5.MD.1** | The student answers none or one part correctly. | The student answers two parts correctly. | The student is able to find all answers correctly but is unable to explain the strategy in Part (c) or answers three of the four parts correctly. | The student correctly:<br><br>a. Estimates 10.357 g to 10.4 g, 12.062 g to 12.1 g, and 7.506 g as 7.5 g; finds the sum 30 g; shows work or model.<br><br>b. Finds the sum 29.925 g and the difference 0.075 g.<br><br>c. Finds the quotient 5.985 g and explains accurately the strategy used.<br><br>d. Rounds 5.985 g to 6 g. |

Name __Ruthie__                           Date __Oct. 2__

1. The following equations involve different quantities and use different operations, yet produce the same result. Use a place value chart and words to explain why this is true.

$$4.13 \times 10^3 = 4130 \qquad 413{,}000 \div 10^2 = 4130$$

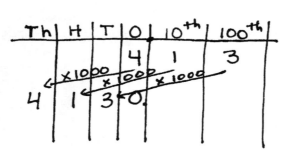 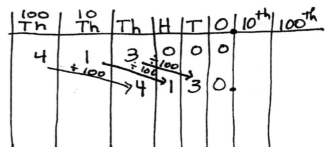

When I multiplied, the digits moved 3 places to the left, because they got larger. When I divided, the digits moved 2 places to the right, because they decreased.

2. Use an area model to explain the product of 4.6 and 3. Write the product in standard form, word form, and expanded form.

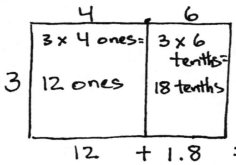

$$12 \quad + 1.8 \quad = 13.8$$

thirteen and eight tenths

$$1 \times 10 + 3 \times 1 + 8 \times \frac{1}{10}$$

       **Module 1:**      Place Value and Decimal Fractions

© 2015 Great Minds. eureka-math.org
G5-M1-TE-B1-1.3.1-1.2016

**EUREKA MATH**

3. Compare using >, <, or =.

a. 2 tenths + 11 hundredths         0.13

b. 13 tenths + 8 tenths + 32 hundredths      2.42

c. 342 hundredths + 7 tenths         3 + 49 hundredths

d. $2 + 31 \times \frac{1}{10} + 14 \times \frac{1}{100}$         2.324

e. $14 + 72 \times \frac{1}{10} + 4 \times \frac{1}{1000}$         21.24

f. $0.3 \times 10^2 + 0.007 \times 10^3$         $0.3 \times 10 + 0.7 \times 10^2$

4. Dr. Mann mixed 10.357 g of chemical A, 12.062 g of chemical B, and 7.506 g of chemical C to make 5 doses of medicine.

a. About how much medicine did he make in grams? Estimate the amount of each chemical by rounding to the nearest tenth of a gram before finding the sum. Show all your thinking.

A   10.357g ≈ 10.4 g

B   12.062g ≈ 12.1 g

C   7.506g ≈ 7.5 g

```
   10.4
   12.1
 +  7.5
 ------
   30.0
```

Dr. Mann made about 30 grams of medicine.

b. Find the actual amount of medicine mixed by Dr. Mann. What is the difference between your estimate and the actual amount?

```
   10.357
   12.062
 +  7.506
 --------
   29.925
```

```
   ³⁰.⁹⁰⁹⁰ 
   30.000
 - 29.925
 --------
    0.075
```

The difference in the estimated and actual amounts is 0.075 grams.

c. How many grams are in one dose of medicine? Explain your strategy for solving this problem.

```
        5.985
    5)29.925
     -25
      ---
       49
      -45
      ---
       42
      -40
      ---
        25
       -25
       ---
         0
```

I used the algorithm to find my answer.

There are 5.985 grams of medicine in one dose.

d. Round the weight of one dose to the nearest gram.

5.985g ≈ 6 g

EUREKA MATH

# Eureka Math® Grade 5 Module 1

Special thanks go to the Gordon A. Cain Center and to the Department of Mathematics at Louisiana State University for their support in the development of *Eureka Math*.

# Mathematics Curriculum

Answer Key

# GRADE 5 • MODULE 1

Place Value and Decimal Fractions

© 2015 Great Minds. eureka-math.org
G5-M1-TE-B1-1.3.1-01.2016

# Lesson 1

## Sprint

### Side A

| | | | | | | | |
|---|---|---|---|---|---|---|---|
| 1. | 120 | 12. | 920 | 23. | 340 | 34. | 560 |
| 2. | 140 | 13. | 180 | 24. | 1,340 | 35. | 4,560 |
| 3. | 150 | 14. | 190 | 25. | 2,340 | 36. | 5,560 |
| 4. | 170 | 15. | 200 | 26. | 3,340 | 37. | 9,500 |
| 5. | 810 | 16. | 300 | 27. | 8,340 | 38. | 9,500 |
| 6. | 810 | 17. | 400 | 28. | 8,340 | 39. | 160 |
| 7. | 210 | 18. | 800 | 29. | 450 | 40. | 600 |
| 8. | 220 | 19. | 800 | 30. | 1,450 | 41. | 4,930 |
| 9. | 230 | 20. | 500 | 31. | 2,450 | 42. | 840 |
| 10. | 290 | 21. | 900 | 32. | 3,450 | 43. | 960 |
| 11. | 920 | 22. | 700 | 33. | 9,450 | 44. | 5,800 |

### Side B

| | | | | | | | |
|---|---|---|---|---|---|---|---|
| 1. | 130 | 12. | 830 | 23. | 430 | 34. | 650 |
| 2. | 140 | 13. | 280 | 24. | 1,430 | 35. | 4,650 |
| 3. | 150 | 14. | 290 | 25. | 2,430 | 36. | 5,650 |
| 4. | 190 | 15. | 300 | 26. | 3,430 | 37. | 9,600 |
| 5. | 910 | 16. | 400 | 27. | 7,430 | 38. | 9,600 |
| 6. | 910 | 17. | 500 | 28. | 7,430 | 39. | 170 |
| 7. | 310 | 18. | 900 | 29. | 540 | 40. | 700 |
| 8. | 320 | 19. | 900 | 30. | 1,540 | 41. | 5,820 |
| 9. | 330 | 20. | 200 | 31. | 2,540 | 42. | 730 |
| 10. | 380 | 21. | 600 | 32. | 3,540 | 43. | 980 |
| 11. | 830 | 22. | 800 | 33. | 8,540 | 44. | 4,700 |

EUREKA MATH

## Problem Set

1.  a. Answer provided

    b. 345.2

    c. 3452

    d. Explanations will vary.

2.  a. Answer provided

    b. 3.45

    c. 0.345

    d. Explanations will vary.

3. 7,234,000; explanations will vary.

4. 320.04
   3200.4 ÷ 10 = 320.04; explanations will vary.

5. 9.5 cm; explanations will vary.

## Exit Ticket

a. 667.1

b. 0.684

## Homework

1.  a. Answer provided

    b. 728.1

    c. 9254

    d. Explanations will vary.

2.  a. Answer provided

    b. 6.78

    c. 0.067

    d. Explanations will vary.

3. 8,912,000

4. 2800.3
   28.003 × 100 = 2800.3; explanations will vary.

5. 251 m; explanations will vary.

Module 1:    Place Value and Decimal Fractions      **255**

# Lesson 2

## Problem Set

1. a. 540,000

   b. 5,400

   c. 87

   d. 0.87

   e. 13

   f. 0.013

   g. 3,120

   h. 40.312

2. a. 193,400

   b. 1,934,000

   c. 19,340,000

   d. Explanations will vary.

3. a. 15.2

   b. 1.52

   c. 0.152

   d. Explanations will vary.

4. Explanations will vary; $\frac{20}{100} = 0.20$, $\frac{2}{1000} = 0.002$

5. 320,000,000 = 10 × 32,000,000; explanations will vary.

## Exit Ticket

1. a. 321

   b. 363.21

2. a. 455,000

   b. 0.455

**EUREKA MATH**

© 2015 Great Minds. eureka-math.org
G5-M1-TE-B1-1.3.1-01.2016

## Homework

1. a. 360,000

   b. 3,600

   c. 43

   d. 0.43

   e. 240

   f. 0.024

   g. 4,540

   h. 30.454

2. a. 145,600

   b. 1,456,000

   c. 14,560,000

   Explanations will vary.

3. a. 1.65

   b. 0.165

   c. Explanations will vary.

4. No; $0.3 \times 100 = 30$; explanations will vary.

5. $1,700,000 \div 10 = 170,000$ km$^2$; explanations will vary.

# Lesson 3

## Sprint

### Side A

| | | | | | | | |
|---|---|---|---|---|---|---|---|
| 1. | 3 | 12. | 21 | 23. | 30 | 34. | 27 |
| 2. | 3 | 13. | 21 | 24. | 27 | 35. | 12 |
| 3. | 6 | 14. | 24 | 25. | 12 | 36. | 9 |
| 4. | 6 | 15. | 24 | 26. | 24 | 37. | 6 |
| 5. | 9 | 16. | 27 | 27. | 15 | 38. | 21 |
| 6. | 12 | 17. | 27 | 28. | 21 | 39. | 24 |
| 7. | 12 | 18. | 30 | 29. | 18 | 40. | 33 |
| 8. | 15 | 19. | 30 | 30. | 30 | 41. | 33 |
| 9. | 15 | 20. | 9 | 31. | 15 | 42. | 36 |
| 10. | 18 | 21. | 3 | 32. | 18 | 43. | 39 |
| 11. | 18 | 22. | 6 | 33. | 3 | 44. | 39 |

### Side B

| | | | | | | | |
|---|---|---|---|---|---|---|---|
| 1. | 3 | 12. | 21 | 23. | 27 | 34. | 12 |
| 2. | 3 | 13. | 21 | 24. | 9 | 35. | 27 |
| 3. | 6 | 14. | 24 | 25. | 24 | 36. | 6 |
| 4. | 6 | 15. | 24 | 26. | 12 | 37. | 21 |
| 5. | 9 | 16. | 27 | 27. | 21 | 38. | 9 |
| 6. | 12 | 17. | 27 | 28. | 15 | 39. | 24 |
| 7. | 12 | 18. | 30 | 29. | 18 | 40. | 33 |
| 8. | 15 | 19. | 30 | 30. | 15 | 41. | 33 |
| 9. | 15 | 20. | 3 | 31. | 30 | 42. | 39 |
| 10. | 18 | 21. | 30 | 32. | 3 | 43. | 39 |
| 11. | 18 | 22. | 6 | 33. | 18 | 44. | 36 |

EUREKA MATH

## Problem Set

1.  a.  $10^4$

    b.  $10^3$

    c.  $10^2$

    d.  $10^4$

    e.  $10^6$

    f.  $10^6$

2.  a.  9,000

    b.  390,000

    c.  72

    d.  7,200

    e.  4,025

    f.  402,500

    g.  0.725

    h.  0.072

3.  Explanations will vary.

4.  Explanations will vary.

5.  a.  3; 300; 3,000

    b.  650; 0.065

    c.  94,300; 943; 0.943

    d.  999,000; 9,990,000; 99,900,000

    e.  0.075; 7,500,000; 750,000,000

    f.  Explanations will vary.

    g.  Explanations will vary.

6.  a.  Explanations will vary.

    b.  Explanations will vary.

## Exit Ticket

1.  a.  $10^3$; $10 \times 10 \times 10$

    b.  $10^4$; $10 \times 10 \times 10 \times 10$

2.  a.  300

    b.  21,600

    c.  0.8

    d.  7.542

© 2015 Great Minds. eureka-math.org
G5-M1-TE-B1-1.3.1-01.2016

**Homework**

1.  a.  $10^3$

    b.  $10^2$

    c.  $10^5$

    d.  $10^3$

    e.  $10^6$

    f.  $10^5$

2.  a.  4,000

    b.  640,000

    c.  53

    d.  5,300

    e.  6,072

    f.  607,200

    g.  0.948

    h.  0.094

3.  a.  2; 200; 2,000

    b.  340; 0.034

    c.  85,700; 857; 0.857

    d.  444,000; 4,440,000; 44,400,000

    e.  0.095; 9,500,000; 950,000,000

4.  Answers will vary; $10^4 = 10 \times 10 \times 10 \times 10 = 10,000$

5.  a.  Answers will vary.

    b.  $247 \div 10^3 = 0.247$; $247 \times 10^3 = 247,000$

**EUREKA MATH**

# Lesson 4

## Problem Set

1.  a.  Answer provided
    b.  $1.05; 105 \div 10^2 = 1.05$
    c.  $1.68; 168; 1.68 \times 10^2 = 168$
    d.  $80; 0.8; 80 \div 10^2 = 0.8$
    e.  $9.2; 920; 9.2 \times 10^2 = 920$
    f.  $4; 0.04; 4 \div 10^2 = 0.04$
    g.  a, c, e

2.  a.  $3; 3,000; 3 \times 10^3 = 3,000$
    b.  $1.2; 1,200; 1.2 \times 10^3 = 1,200$
    c.  $1,020; 1.02; 1,020 \div 10^3 = 1.02$
    d.  $97; 0.097; 97 \div 10^3 = 0.097$
    e.  $7.28; 7,280; 7.28 \times 10^3 = 7,280$
    f.  $4; 0.004; 4 \div 10^3 = 0.004$
    g.  c, d, f

3.  a.  3,512
    b.  $0.08; 8 \div 10^2 = 0.08$
    c.  $0.042; 42 \div 10^3 = 0.042$
    d.  $50; 0.05 \times 10^3 = 50$
    e.  $0.2; 0.002 \times 10^2 = 0.2$

4.  $4.75 \text{ m} = 4,750 \text{ mm}; 475 \times 10^3 = 4,750$

5.  $1 \text{ cm} = 0.01 \text{ m}; 1 \div 10^2 = 0.01$

6.  Explanations will vary.

## Exit Ticket

1.  a.  $200; 2 \times 10^2 = 200$
    b.  $0.04; 40 \div 10^3 = 0.04$

2.  a.  390 cm
    b.  0.04 m

© 2015 Great Minds. eureka-math.org
G5-M1-TE-B1-1.3.1-01.2016

## Homework

1.  a.  Answer provided
    b.  1.08; $108 \div 10^2 = 1.08$
    c.  2.49; 249; $2.49 \times 10^2 = 249$
    d.  50; 0.50; $50 \div 10^2 = 0.5$
    e.  6.3; 630; $6.3 \times 10^2 = 630$
    f.  7; 0.07; $7 \div 10^2 = 0.07$
    g.  b, d, f

2.  a.  4; 4000; $4 \times 10^3 = 4,000$
    b.  1.7; 1,700; $1.7 \times 10^3 = 1,700$
    c.  1,050; 1.05; $1,050 \div 10^3 = 1.05$
    d.  65; 0.065; $65 \div 10^3 = 0.065$
    e.  4.92; 4,920; $4.92 \times 10^3 = 4,920$
    f.  3; 0.003; $3 \div 10^3 = 0.003$
    g.  a, b, e

3.  a.  2,638; answer provided
    b.  0.07; $7 \div 10^2 = 0.07$
    c.  0.039; $39 \div 10^3 = 0.039$
    d.  80; $0.08 \times 10^3 = 80$
    e.  0.5; $0.005 \times 10^2 = 0.5$

4.  1.49 m = 1,490 mm; $1.49 \times 10^3 = 1,490$

5.  2 cm = 0.02 m; $2 \div 10^2 = 0.02$

6.  77 mm = 0.077 m; $77 \div 10^3 = 0.077$

EUREKA
MATH

# Lesson 5

## Sprint

### Side A

| | | | | | | | |
|---|---|---|---|---|---|---|---|
| 1. | 623 | 12. | 300 | 23. | 4,100 | 34. | 91.9 |
| 2. | 6,230 | 13. | 0.2 | 24. | 7,600 | 35. | 1,820 |
| 3. | 62,300 | 14. | 2 | 25. | 10 | 36. | 14,700 |
| 4. | 736 | 15. | 20 | 26. | 70 | 37. | 202.1 |
| 5. | 7,360 | 16. | 0.08 | 27. | 7.2 | 38. | 1,721 |
| 6. | 73,600 | 17. | 0.8 | 28. | 8.02 | 39. | 64 |
| 7. | 6 | 18. | 8 | 29. | 19 | 40. | 82 |
| 8. | 0.6 | 19. | 3.2 | 30. | 7,412 | 41. | 96 |
| 9. | 0.06 | 20. | 6.7 | 31. | 680 | 42. | 39 |
| 10. | 3 | 21. | 91 | 32. | 49.01 | 43. | 124.8 |
| 11. | 30 | 22. | 74 | 33. | 1,607 | 44. | 564.8 |

### Side B

| | | | | | | | |
|---|---|---|---|---|---|---|---|
| 1. | 461 | 12. | 900 | 23. | 5,200 | 34. | 81.8 |
| 2. | 4,610 | 13. | 0.4 | 24. | 8,700 | 35. | 2,930 |
| 3. | 46,100 | 14. | 4 | 25. | 10 | 36. | 25,800 |
| 4. | 892 | 15. | 40 | 26. | 80 | 37. | 303.2 |
| 5. | 8,920 | 16. | 0.07 | 27. | 0.83 | 38. | 2,831 |
| 6. | 89,200 | 17. | 0.7 | 28. | 9.03 | 39. | 42 |
| 7. | 3 | 18. | 7 | 29. | 17 | 40. | 66 |
| 8. | 0.3 | 19. | 4.5 | 30. | 8,523 | 41. | 93 |
| 9. | 0.03 | 20. | 7.8 | 31. | 790 | 42. | 36 |
| 10. | 9 | 21. | 28 | 32. | 58.02 | 43. | 84.4 |
| 11. | 90 | 22. | 19 | 33. | 2,708 | 44. | 524.4 |

## Problem Set

1.  a.  Answer provided
    b.  0.024
    c.  1.324
    d.  0.608
    e.  600.008
    f.  0.046
    g.  3.946
    h.  200.904

2.  a.  Five thousandths
    b.  Eleven and thirty-seven thousandths
    c.  Four hundred three and six hundred eight thousandths

3.  a.  Answer provided
    b.  $2 \times \frac{1}{10} + 4 \times \frac{1}{100} + 9 \times \frac{1}{1000}$
    c.  $5 \times 10 + 7 \times 1 + 2 \times \frac{1}{10} + 8 \times \frac{1}{100} + 1 \times \frac{1}{1000}$

4.  a.  74.692
    b.  530.809
    c.  4,207.034

5.  Both of them; explanations will vary.

## Exit Ticket

1.  0.009

2.  $\frac{29}{1000}$

3.  Twenty-four and three hundred fifty-seven thousandths

    a.  $2 \times 10 + 4 \times 1 + 3 \times 0.1 + 5 \times 0.01 + 7 \times 0.001$
    b.  2 tens 4 ones 3 tenths 5 hundredths 7 thousandths

EUREKA
MATH

## Homework

1.  a.  Answer provided
    b.  0.035
    c.  9.235
    d.  800.005
    e.  0.008
    f.  0.028
    g.  7.528
    h.  300.502

2.  a.  Eight thousandths
    b.  Fifteen and sixty-two thousandths
    c.  Six hundred seven and four hundred nine thousandths

3.  a.  Answer provided
    b.  $3 \times 0.1 + 6 \times 0.01 + 2 \times 0.001$
    c.  $4 \times 10 + 9 \times 1 + 5 \times 0.1 + 6 \times 0.01 + 4 \times 0.001$

4.  a.  35.276
    b.  920.307
    c.  5,408.065

5.  a.  $4 \times 1 + 8 \times \frac{1}{10} + 7 \times \frac{1}{100} + 5 \times \frac{1}{1000}$
    b.  $3 \times 1 + 1 \times \frac{1}{10} + 2 \times \frac{1}{100} + 5 \times \frac{1}{1000}$

6.  Nancy: $4 \times 100 + 1 \times 10 + 2 \times 1 + 6 \times \frac{1}{10} + 3 \times \frac{1}{100} + 8 \times \frac{1}{1000}$

    Charles: $4 \times 100 + 1 \times 10 + 2 \times 1 + 6 \times 0.1 + 3 \times 0.01 + 8 \times 0.001$

# Lesson 6

## Problem Set

1. <; >; completed place value chart; explanations will vary.

2. a. <
   b. =
   c. =
   d. =
   e. >
   f. =
   g. >
   h. <
   i. <
   j. <
   k. <

3. a. 3.04; 3.049; 3.05; 3.059
   b. 182.025; 182.05; 182.105; 182.205

4. a. 7.68; 7.608; 7.6; 7.068
   b. 439.612; 439.261; 439.216; 439.126

5. No; answers will vary; Angel has $\frac{500}{1000}$ L, but Lance has $\frac{485}{1000}$ L.

6. Dr. Hong prescribes the most; Dr. Evans prescribes the least; explanations will vary.

## Exit Ticket

1. <
2. <

3. 76.343; 76.342; 76.332; 76.232

## Homework

1. a. <
   b. =
   c. =
   d. <
   e. >
   f. =
   g. <
   h. >
   i. <
   j. <

2. a. 8.008; 8.08; 8.081; 8.09
   b. 14.200; 14.204; 14.210; 14.240

3. a. 8.58; 8.508; 7.5; 7.058
   b. 439.612; 439.261; 439.216; 439.126

4. James's hand was bigger; explanations will vary.

5. Salvador's plane traveled the farthest distance; Jennifer's plane traveled the shortest distance; explanations will vary.

EUREKA MATH

# Lesson 7

## Sprint

### Side A

| | | | | | | | |
|---|---|---|---|---|---|---|---|
| 1. | 5 | 12. | 0.35 | 23. | 8.55 | 34. | 0.085 |
| 2. | 0.5 | 13. | 0.75 | 24. | 2.85 | 35. | 0.095 |
| 3. | 0.005 | 14. | 0.15 | 25. | 0.035 | 36. | 26.5 |
| 4. | 15 | 15. | 0.015 | 26. | 0.135 | 37. | 7.85 |
| 5. | 1.5 | 16. | 0.025 | 27. | 0.375 | 38. | 1.265 |
| 6. | 2.5 | 17. | 0.035 | 28. | 85 | 39. | 29.5 |
| 7. | 3.5 | 18. | 0.075 | 29. | 95 | 40. | 9.95 |
| 8. | 7.5 | 19. | 6.5 | 30. | 8.5 | 41. | 7.95 |
| 9. | 1.5 | 20. | 16.5 | 31. | 9.5 | 42. | 1.595 |
| 10. | 0.15 | 21. | 38.5 | 32. | 0.85 | 43. | 1.795 |
| 11. | 0.25 | 22. | 0.45 | 33. | 0.95 | 44. | 3.995 |

### Side B

| | | | | | | | |
|---|---|---|---|---|---|---|---|
| 1. | 15 | 12. | 0.25 | 23. | 0.75 | 34. | 0.95 |
| 2. | 1.5 | 13. | 0.35 | 24. | 4.75 | 35. | 0.085 |
| 3. | 0.15 | 14. | 0.65 | 25. | 2.35 | 36. | 0.095 |
| 4. | 0.015 | 15. | 0.15 | 26. | 0.025 | 37. | 36.5 |
| 5. | 5 | 16. | 0.015 | 27. | 0.125 | 38. | 6.85 |
| 6. | 0.5 | 17. | 0.025 | 28. | 0.475 | 39. | 1.465 |
| 7. | 1.5 | 18. | 0.035 | 29. | 85 | 40. | 39.5 |
| 8. | 2.5 | 19. | 0.065 | 30. | 95 | 41. | 9.95 |
| 9. | 6.5 | 20. | 7.5 | 31. | 8.5 | 42. | 6.95 |
| 10. | 1.5 | 21. | 17.5 | 32. | 9.5 | 43. | 1.295 |
| 11. | 0.15 | 22. | 47.5 | 33. | 0.85 | 44. | 6.995 |

## Problem Set

1. 3 ones + 1 tenth; 31 tenths; 310 hundredths
   a. 310 hundredths = 3.1
   b. 31 tenths = 3.1
   c. 0 tens

2. 11 tens + 5 ones + 3 tenths + 7 hundredths + 6 thousandths; 115 ones + 3 tenths + 7 hundredths + 6 thousandths; 1,153 tenths + 7 hundredths + 6 thousandths; 11,537 hundredths + 6 thousandths
   a. 11,538 hundredths = 115.38
   b. 115 ones = 115
   c. 12 tens = 120

3. 9 tenths + 9 hundredths + 4 thousandths; 99 hundredths + 4 thousandths; 944 thousandths
   a. 99 hundredths = 0.99
   b. 10 tenths = 1.0
   c. 1 one = 1
   d. 0 tens = 0

4. 2.14 m

5. Explanations will vary.

## Exit Ticket

a. 855 hundredths = 8.55
b. 1 ten = 10

## Homework

1. 4 ones + 3 tenths; 43 tenths; 430 hundredths
   a. 430 hundredths = 4.3
   b. 43 tenths = 4.3
   c. 4 ones = 4

2. 22 tens + 5 ones + 2 tenths + 8 hundredths + 6 thousandths; 225 ones + 2 tenths + 8 hundredths + 6 ones; 2,252 tenths + 8 hundredths + 6 thousandths
   a. 22,529 hundredths = 225.29
   b. 225 ones = 225
   c. 23 tens = 230

3. 8 ones + 9 tenths + 8 hundredths + 4 thousandths; 89 tenths + 8 hundredths + 4 thousandths; 898 hundredths + 4 thousandths
   a. 898 hundredths = 8.98
   b. 90 tenths = 9.0
   c. 9 ones = 9
   d. 1 ten = 10

4. a. 18.39 m
   b. 1,838.6 cm

5. Explanations will vary.

EUREKA MATH

# Lesson 8

## Problem Set

1.  a.  32.7; 32.70; 33

    b.  142.0; 142.00; 140; 100

2.  1,325.5

3.  a.  13.74; explanations will vary.

    b.  13.65; explanations will vary.

## Exit Ticket

a.  14.0

b.  382.99

## Homework

1.  a.  43.6; 43.59; 44

    b.  243.9; 243.88; 240; 200

2.  285.2 miles

3.  a.  18.64; explanations will vary.

    b.  18.55; explanations will vary.

# Lesson 9

## Sprint

### Side A

| | | | | | | | |
|---|---|---|---|---|---|---|---|
| 1. | 3 | 12. | 9 | 23. | 13 | 34. | 50 |
| 2. | 3 | 13. | 10 | 24. | 17 | 35. | 3 |
| 3. | 3 | 14. | 20 | 25. | 17 | 36. | 17 |
| 4. | 3 | 15. | 30 | 26. | 12 | 37. | 12 |
| 5. | 4 | 16. | 90 | 27. | 11 | 38. | 5 |
| 6. | 4 | 17. | 2 | 28. | 13 | 39. | 13 |
| 7. | 4 | 18. | 2 | 29. | 14 | 40. | 60 |
| 8. | 14 | 19. | 2 | 30. | 16 | 41. | 5 |
| 9. | 13 | 20. | 2 | 31. | 15 | 42. | 19 |
| 10. | 14 | 21. | 2 | 32. | 6 | 43. | 20 |
| 11. | 8 | 22. | 3 | 33. | 8 | 44. | 70 |

### Side B

| | | | | | | | |
|---|---|---|---|---|---|---|---|
| 1. | 4 | 12. | 9 | 23. | 14 | 34. | 40 |
| 2. | 4 | 13. | 10 | 24. | 18 | 35. | 4 |
| 3. | 4 | 14. | 20 | 25. | 18 | 36. | 18 |
| 4. | 4 | 15. | 30 | 26. | 13 | 37. | 13 |
| 5. | 5 | 16. | 80 | 27. | 12 | 38. | 6 |
| 6. | 5 | 17. | 3 | 28. | 14 | 39. | 14 |
| 7. | 5 | 18. | 3 | 29. | 15 | 40. | 50 |
| 8. | 15 | 19. | 3 | 30. | 17 | 41. | 6 |
| 9. | 14 | 20. | 3 | 31. | 16 | 42. | 19 |
| 10. | 15 | 21. | 3 | 32. | 7 | 43. | 20 |
| 11. | 8 | 22. | 4 | 33. | 9 | 44. | 60 |

EUREKA MATH

## Problem Set

1. a. 3; 0.3
   b. 23; 2; 3; 2.3
   c. 3; 0.03
   d. 32; 3; 2; 0.32
   e. 3; 0.003
   f. 43; 4; 3; 0.043
   g. 603; 0.603
   h. 76; 7.6
   i. 9007; 9.007

2. a. 1.12
   b. 1.11
   c. 10.1
   d. 59.11
   e. 66.901
   f. 97.900

3. a. 2.542; 2.300
   b. 6.122 km

4. Pedometer and math apps; explanations will vary.

## Exit Ticket

1. a. 12; 1; 2
   b. 72; 7; 2

2. a. 4.20
   b. 44.92

## Homework

1. a. 7
   b. 21; 2; 1
   c. 7
   d. 34; 3; 4
   e. 7
   f. 44; 4; 4
   g. 507
   h. 48
   i. 6,016

2. a. 1.1
   b. 2.11
   c. 10.1
   d. 59.11
   e. 77.701
   f. 97.900

3. a. 4,133 km
   b. 4.126 km

4. $12.86

# Lesson 10

## Problem Set

1.  a.  3; 0.3
    b.  3; 9; 3.009
    c.  7; 4; 700.04
    d.  21; 0.021

2.  a.  0.7
    b.  90.79
    c.  180.77
    d.  7.078
    e.  58.054
    f.  358.469

3.  a.  89.9
    b.  0.8
    c.  2.5
    d.  4.69
    e.  5.592
    f.  1.81

4.  No; explanations will vary; 0.47

5.  $0.37

## Exit Ticket

1.  17; 8; 9; 0.9

2.  a.  56.077
    b.  6.65

## Homework

1.  a.  6
    b.  6; 2
    c.  4; 3
    d.  33; 3; 3

2.  a.  0.9
    b.  40.94
    c.  319.92
    d.  5.092
    e.  46.166
    f.  737.09

3.  a.  269.7
    b.  3.4
    c.  1.1
    d.  3.77
    e.  8.196
    f.  4.77

4.  No; explanations will vary; 0.75

5.  $3.89

EUREKA
MATH

# Lesson 11

## Problem Set

1.  a.  $3 \times 0.2 = 0.6$
    b.  $5 \times 0.02 = 0.1$
    c.  $3 \times 0.6 = 1.8$
    d.  $6 \times 0.04 = 0.24$
    e.  $5 \times 0.7 = 3.5$
    f.  $0.004 \times 3 = 0.012$

2.  a.  21; 0.7; 21.84
    b.  $24 + 1.2 + 0.3 = 25.5$
    c.  $12 + 1.8 + 0.15 = 13.95$
    d.  $80 + 0.28 + 0.02 = 80.3$

3.  Models will vary; 18.2

4.  $8.80

## Exit Ticket

1.  $4 \times 0.3 = 1.2$

2.  9 ones; 6 tenths; 3 hundredths; 3; 9; 6; 3; 27 ones + 18 tenths + 9 hundredths = 28.89

## Homework

1.  a.  $2 \times 0.4 = 0.8$
    b.  $4 \times 0.05 = 0.2$
    c.  $4 \times 0.7 = 2.8$
    d.  $3 \times 0.05 = 0.15$
    e.  $9 \times 0.7 = 6.3$
    f.  $8 \times 0.006 = 0.048$

2.  a.  24; 2.8; 0.36; 27.16
    b.  $42 + 2.4 + 0.54 = 44.94$
    c.  $27 + 5.4 + 0.45 = 32.85$
    d.  $60 + 0.3 + 0.21 + 0.015 = 60.525$

3.  No; area models will vary; 34.4

4.  $16.39

# Lesson 12

## Sprint

### Side A

| | | | | | | | |
|---|---|---|---|---|---|---|---|
| 1. | 4 | 12. | 42.5 | 23. | 5.1 | 34. | 3.594 |
| 2. | 4.5 | 13. | 42.58 | 24. | 5.8 | 35. | 3.585 |
| 3. | 4.52 | 14. | 41.789 | 25. | 5.83 | 36. | 3.684 |
| 4. | 0.4 | 15. | 5 | 26. | 5.836 | 37. | 4.584 |
| 5. | 0.47 | 16. | 5.6 | 27. | 6.736 | 38. | 6.814 |
| 6. | 5.47 | 17. | 5.62 | 28. | 5.746 | 39. | 8.643 |
| 7. | 0.04 | 18. | 5.628 | 29. | 5.737 | 40. | 7.651 |
| 8. | 0.84 | 19. | 4.728 | 30. | 6.218 | 41. | 4.087 |
| 9. | 2.84 | 20. | 4.638 | 31. | 3.01 | 42. | 4.28 |
| 10. | 40 | 21. | 4.629 | 32. | 3.51 | 43. | 13.589 |
| 11. | 42 | 22. | 27.148 | 33. | 3.59 | 44. | 15.501 |

### Side B

| | | | | | | | |
|---|---|---|---|---|---|---|---|
| 1. | 3 | 12. | 33.5 | 23. | 4.1 | 34. | 2.594 |
| 2. | 3.5 | 13. | 33.58 | 24. | 4.8 | 35. | 2.585 |
| 3. | 3.53 | 14. | 31.789 | 25. | 4.83 | 36. | 2.684 |
| 4. | 0.3 | 15. | 4 | 26. | 4.836 | 37. | 3.584 |
| 5. | 0.37 | 16. | 4.6 | 27. | 5.736 | 38. | 5.814 |
| 6. | 5.37 | 17. | 4.62 | 28. | 4.746 | 39. | 7.643 |
| 7. | 0.03 | 18. | 4.628 | 29. | 4.737 | 40. | 6.751 |
| 8. | 0.83 | 19. | 3.728 | 30. | 5.218 | 41. | 3.087 |
| 9. | 4.83 | 20. | 3.638 | 31. | 2.01 | 42. | 3.280 |
| 10. | 30 | 21. | 3.629 | 32. | 2.51 | 43. | 12.589 |
| 11. | 33 | 22. | 37.148 | 33. | 2.59 | 44. | 14.401 |

EUREKA MATH

## Problem Set

1.  a.  Circle 10; answers will vary.

    b.  Circle 21.98; answers will vary.

    c.  Circle 48.176; answers will vary.

    d.  Circle 49.32; answers will vary.

2.  2.20 m; 3 m; answers will vary.

3.  ≈ 14 km; 14.48 km; accurate work shown

4.  80 × 5 is about $400; answers will vary.

## Exit Ticket

1.  a.  Circle 10.2

    b.  Circle 35.72

2.  About 42; answers will vary.

## Homework

1.  a.  Circle 6.3; answers will vary.

    b.  Circle 25.62; answers will vary.

    c.  Circle 42.371; answers will vary.

    d.  Circle 43.38; answers will vary.

2.  33.2 kg

3.  $128.49

4.  $50.64

# Lesson 13

## Sprint

### Side A

| | | | | | | | |
|---|---|---|---|---|---|---|---|
| 1. | 4.0 | 12. | 8.139 | 23. | 7.983 | 34. | 6.122 |
| 2. | 4.9 | 13. | 0.04 | 24. | 7.981 | 35. | 9.342 |
| 3. | 4.93 | 14. | 0.047 | 25. | 2.6 | 36. | 8.047 |
| 4. | 4.932 | 15. | 1.047 | 26. | 2.685 | 37. | 9.107 |
| 5. | 3.932 | 16. | 1.847 | 27. | 2.285 | 38. | 6.870 |
| 6. | 1.932 | 17. | 1.837 | 28. | 4.513 | 39. | 4.548 |
| 7. | 0.4 | 18. | 1.817 | 29. | 3.57 | 40. | 6.348 |
| 8. | 0.43 | 19. | 0.004 | 30. | 3.576 | 41. | 6.528 |
| 9. | 0.439 | 20. | 7.004 | 31. | 3.536 | 42. | 6.546 |
| 10. | 8.439 | 21. | 7.904 | 32. | 7.942 | 43. | 6.136 |
| 11. | 8.339 | 22. | 7.984 | 33. | 6.125 | 44. | 9.513 |

### Side B

| | | | | | | | |
|---|---|---|---|---|---|---|---|
| 1. | 5.0 | 12. | 8.239 | 23. | 7.984 | 34. | 7.123 |
| 2. | 5.9 | 13. | 0.05 | 24. | 7.982 | 35. | 1.453 |
| 3. | 5.93 | 14. | 0.057 | 25. | 3.6 | 36. | 8.057 |
| 4. | 5.932 | 15. | 1.057 | 26. | 3.685 | 37. | 1.207 |
| 5. | 4.932 | 16. | 1.857 | 27. | 3.285 | 38. | 7.98 |
| 6. | 2.932 | 17. | 1.847 | 28. | 5.524 | 39. | 5.548 |
| 7. | 0.5 | 18. | 1.827 | 29. | 4.57 | 40. | 7.348 |
| 8. | 0.53 | 19. | 0.005 | 30. | 4.576 | 41. | 7.528 |
| 9. | 0.539 | 20. | 7.005 | 31. | 4.536 | 42. | 7.546 |
| 10. | 8.539 | 21. | 7.905 | 32. | 6.143 | 43. | 7.137 |
| 11. | 8.439 | 22. | 7.985 | 33. | 7.126 | 44. | 1.623 |

EUREKA MATH

## Problem Set

1.  a.  4; 0.4
    b.  4; 0.04
    c.  12; 0.012
    d.  4; 0.4

2.  a.  42; 6; 0.6
    b.  2; 64; 1; 32; 1.32
    c.  12; 64; 6; 32; 6.32
    d.  42; 6; 7 tenths + 1 hundredth; 0.71
    e.  42 tenths ÷ 6 + 36 thousandths ÷ 6; 7 tenths + 6 thousandths; 0.706

3.  a.  4; 0.4
    b.  9; 0.009

4.  a.  No; explanations may vary.
    b.  No; explanations may vary.
    c.  Yes; explanations may vary.

5.  3.12 doses or 3 full doses

6.  $0.41

## Exit Ticket

1.  a.  9; 0.9
    b.  8; 0.08
    c.  3; 0.003

2.  a.  45; 9; 0.9
    b.  6; 12; 1; 2; 1.02

## Homework

1.  a.  5; 0.5
    b.  4; 0.04
    c.  9; 0.009

2.  a.  9; 36; 3; 12; 3.12
    b.  36; 12; 12; 4; 12.004
    c.  35; 5; 7 tenths + 1 hundredth; 0.71
    d.  35 tenths ÷ 5 + 45 thousandths ÷ 5; 7 tenths + 9 thousandths; 0.709

3.  a.  3; 0.3
    b.  6; 0.006

4.  a.  No; explanations may vary.
    b.  Yes; explanations may vary.
    c.  No; explanations may vary.

5.  $1.21

6.  6.32 L

© 2015 Great Minds. eureka-math.org
G5-M1-TE-B1-1.3.1-01.2016

# Lesson 14

## Problem Set

1.   a.   1.412

     b.   0.662

2.   a.   0.26

     b.   1.82

     c.   3.49

3.   Explanations will vary; 0.21

4.   0.37 m

5.   $0.12; accurate tape diagram shown

## Exit Ticket

1.   2.686

2.   0.144

## Homework

1.   a.   1.747

     b.   1.343

2.   a.   0.16

     b.   1.29

     c.   2.734

3.   $13.56

4.   0.4 lb

EUREKA MATH

# Lesson 15

## Sprint

### Side A

| | | | | | | | |
|---|---|---|---|---|---|---|---|
| 1. | 100 | 12. | 4,000 | 23. | 2,400 | 34. | 914,000 |
| 2. | 100 | 13. | 4,000 | 24. | 2,470 | 35. | 911,040 |
| 3. | 1,000 | 14. | 4,200 | 25. | 2,407 | 36. | 911,070 |
| 4. | 1,000 | 15. | 4,280 | 26. | 2,400.7 | 37. | 120 |
| 5. | 10,000 | 16. | 4,283 | 27. | 53,000 | 38. | 350 |
| 6. | 10,000 | 17. | 50,000 | 28. | 53,000 | 39. | 54,920 |
| 7. | 300 | 18. | 50,000 | 29. | 53,800 | 40. | 8,040 |
| 8. | 300 | 19. | 57,000 | 30. | 53,080 | 41. | 71,090 |
| 9. | 310 | 20. | 57,300 | 31. | 53,082 | 42. | 5.8 |
| 10. | 315 | 21. | 57,310 | 32. | 91,000 | 43. | 20,780 |
| 11. | 315.7 | 22. | 2,400 | 33. | 91,000 | 44. | 42,007.9 |

### Side B

| | | | | | | | |
|---|---|---|---|---|---|---|---|
| 1. | 100 | 12. | 5,000 | 23. | 4,200 | 34. | 814,000 |
| 2. | 100 | 13. | 5,000 | 24. | 4,270 | 35. | 811,040 |
| 3. | 1,000 | 14. | 5,200 | 25. | 4,207 | 36. | 811,070 |
| 4. | 1,000 | 15. | 5,280 | 26. | 4,200.7 | 37. | 130 |
| 5. | 10,000 | 16. | 5,283 | 27. | 35,000 | 38. | 530 |
| 6. | 10,000 | 17. | 70,000 | 28. | 35,000 | 39. | 43,910 |
| 7. | 400 | 18. | 70,000 | 29. | 35,800 | 40. | 7,030 |
| 8. | 400 | 19. | 75,000 | 30. | 35,080 | 41. | 61,090 |
| 9. | 410 | 20. | 75,300 | 31. | 35,082 | 42. | 8.5 |
| 10. | 415 | 21. | 75,310 | 32. | 81,000 | 43. | 30,870 |
| 11. | 415.7 | 22. | 4,200 | 33. | 81,000 | 44. | 53,009.7 |

## Problem Set

1. a. 0.25
   b. 1.425
2. a. 0.45
   b. 1.82
   c. 1.5
   d. 0.245
   e. 1.55
   f. 22.75

3. 1.25 kg
4. 3.25 L

## Exit Ticket

1. 0.225
2. 1.96

## Homework

1. a. 0.175
   b. 1.62
2. a. 0.35
   b. 0.65
   c. 2.25
   d. 0.46
   e. 2.35
   f. 11.375

3. 1.74 m
4. 1.425 gal

Module 1: Place Value and Decimal Fractions

EUREKA MATH

# Lesson 16

## Sprint

### Side A

| | | | | |
|---|---|---|---|---|
| 1. | 100 | 12. | 4,000 | 23. | 34 | 34. | 8.14 |
| 2. | 100 | 13. | 4,000 | 24. | 34.7 | 35. | 8.104 |
| 3. | 1,000 | 14. | 4,200 | 25. | 34.07 | 36. | 9.107 |
| 4. | 1,000 | 15. | 4,280 | 26. | 34.007 | 37. | 1.2 |
| 5. | 10,000 | 16. | 4,283 | 27. | 63 | 38. | 0.35 |
| 6. | 10,000 | 17. | 50,000 | 28. | 63 | 39. | 4.592 |
| 7. | 300 | 18. | 50,000 | 29. | 63.8 | 40. | 6.04 |
| 8. | 300 | 19. | 57,000 | 30. | 63.08 | 41. | 6.108 |
| 9. | 310 | 20. | 57,300 | 31. | 63.082 | 42. | 0.078 |
| 10. | 315 | 21. | 57,310 | 32. | 8.1 | 43. | 40.87 |
| 11. | 315.7 | 22. | 2,400 | 33. | 8.1 | 44. | 520.709 |

### Side B

| | | | | |
|---|---|---|---|---|
| 1. | 100 | 12. | 6 | 23. | 43 | 34. | 9.14 |
| 2. | 100 | 13. | 6 | 24. | 43.7 | 35. | 9.104 |
| 3. | 1,000 | 14. | 6.2 | 25. | 43.07 | 36. | 8.107 |
| 4. | 1,000 | 15. | 6.28 | 26. | 43.007 | 37. | 1.7 |
| 5. | 10,000 | 16. | 6.283 | 27. | 73 | 38. | 0.45 |
| 6. | 10,000 | 17. | 7 | 28. | 73 | 39. | 5.492 |
| 7. | 5 | 18. | 7 | 29. | 73.8 | 40. | 4.06 |
| 8. | 5 | 19. | 7.6 | 30. | 73.08 | 41. | 7.108 |
| 9. | 5.1 | 20. | 7.63 | 31. | 73.082 | 42. | 0.087 |
| 10. | 5.16 | 21. | 7.631 | 32. | 9.1 | 43. | 60.47 |
| 11. | 5.167 | 22. | 43 | 33. | 9.1 | 44. | 720.509 |

## Problem Set

1.  a.  $31.50
    b.  $42
2.  Ava: 112 cm
    Olivia: 89 cm
3.  $96.01

4.  1.675 lb
5.  a.  8.85 kg
    b.  3; explanations will vary.

## Exit Ticket

Word problems will vary; Jim's dog weighs 5.41 lb; $\frac{2}{3}$ of John's dog's weight is 10.82 lb.

## Homework

1.  6.55 m
2.  a.  $127.05
    b.  $1,172.95

3.  9.73 lb
4.  0.744 L

EUREKA
MATH